FEEDING C

FEEDING CAGE BIRDS

A Manual of
Diets for Aviculture

Kenton C. Lint and
Alice Marie Lint

BLANDFORD PRESS
LONDON · NEW YORK · SYDNEY

This edition first published in the UK 1988 by Blandford Press
Artillery House, Artillery Row, London SW1P 1RT.

Originally published by Blandford Books Ltd 1981

Distributed in the United States by
Sterling Publishing Co. Inc.
2 Park Avenue, New York, NY 10016

Distributed in Australia by
Capricorn Link (Australia) Pty Ltd
PO Box 665, Lane Cove, NSW 2066

ISBN 0 7137 2014 X

Printed in England
by Biddles, Guildford

CONTENTS

*To Evelyn and Roland
with love and appreciation for their
encouragement and understanding*

PREFACE

Since earliest times birds have played an important role in the lives of men. Some have provided him with food. Others have added colour, song and companionship to enhance the quality of his life. Birds have added immeasurably to man's knowledge of aerodynamics. Without birds, life would indeed be poorer.

The acquisition of birds—whether one or hundreds—places a grave responsibility on the acquirer. The bird in captivity is solely dependent on its owner, and we have found that the true bird lover is anxious to provide the best possible environment for his charge.

Today, with our ever-increasing awareness of the precarious state of much of life on our earth, we have an even greater responsibility to the birds in our care. To that end, we have included not only diets but a brief description of the birds—what they look like, where they live, their life styles and native foods. It is hoped that this will encourage better husbandry, increased propagation of the birds which are in captivity and thus encourage the conservation of those which are still in the wild.

We are grateful to the several Directors of the Zoological Society of San Diego under whom we have served, and to the members of the Board of Trustees, who through the years have been committed to maintaining the highest standards of care for the wild life in their care. They have encouraged and expected the same commitment on the part of the staff and keepers.

We are also grateful to the many persons, both lay and professional, who have shared their knowledge and experiences and love of birds with us. We are especially grateful to Dr Jean Delacour, Dr Dennis Fox, Dr Robert E. Feeny, Rosemary Low and Frank Todd, who insisted that the book must be written, and to Judi Myers without whose corrections and typing it might never have been completed.

K. C. L. and A. M. L.

NOTE ON AVAILABILITY OF FOODS

Alternatives have been given in most cases for natural foods and American brand-name products which are not available in all parts of the world. Where this has not proved to be possible, the constituents of certain products have been listed in detail in Appendix I. At the end of this Appendix, there is a list of British sources of those products which are not generally available in the UK. There is also a list of equivalent Australian products and their suppliers.

Appendix II gives instructions on the propagation of live foods mentioned in the text.

Sphenisciformes

PENGUINS

Most authorities recognize fifteen species of penguins in a single family of flightless, swimming birds of the coasts and waters of the southern hemisphere. The penguins are a very primitive group, highly specialized for a marine existence.

Penguins, as well as many sea birds, are subject to salt depletion in captivity. These birds have large supranasal salt glands which supplement the salt excretion function of their kidneys. When stressed, the birds involuntarily over-excrete salt from the nasal glands. If the salt is not replenished in their water or food, the birds' condition deteriorates rapidly.

Daily Diets for Penguins (1)

Penguins Sphenisciformes	Fish Pacific Mackerel (230 g)	Squid	Fish Smelt (Whitebait)	Fish Herring	Fish Trout	Salt—NaCl Supplement Thermotab capsule (1 g)
Emperor (*Aptenodytes* *forsteri*)	9 am (6) 4 pm (6)	9 am (4) 4 pm (4)			Ailing bird off feed (1) 230 g	Capsule inserted in mouth of 1 fish daily
King (*Aptenodytes* *patagonicus*)	9 am (6) 4 pm (6)	9 am (4) 4 pm (4)			Ailing bird off feed (1) 230 g	Capsule inserted in mouth of 1 fish daily
Gentoo (*Pygoscelis* *papua*)	9 am (2) 4 pm (2)	9 am (4) 4 pm (4)	9 am (6) 4 pm (6)		Ailing bird off feed (1) 230 g	Capsule inserted in mouth of 1 fish daily
Macaroni (*Eudyptes* *chrysolophus*)		9 am (6) 4 pm (6)	9 am (6) 4 pm (6)			Capsule inserted in mouth of 1 fish daily
Rockhopper (*Eudyptes* *crestatus*)		9 am (6) 4 pm (6)	9 am (6) 4 pm (6)			Capsule inserted in mouth of 1 fish daily

All feed in the sea on fish, squid and crustaceans. This group is included to enable readers to feed orphaned penguins properly. From time to time, fishing boats bring penguins into port which they have released from en-tanglement in fishing nets. When first captured, many penguins present a special feeding problem, as they persistently refuse to eat anything other than live fish. Thus it is necessary to force-feed them by hand, often for long periods, before they eventually accept dead fish tossed on a deck or thrown into their swimming pool or tank.

Daily Diets for Penguins (2)

Penguins Sphenisciformes	Fish Herring	Fish Smelt (Whitebait)	Squid	Fish Sardines	Salt—NaCL Supplement Thermotab capsule (1 g)
Humboldt (*Spheniscus humboldti*)	9.30 am (10) 4 pm (10)	9.30 am (4) 4 pm (4)	9.30 am (6) 4 pm (6)	9.30 am (2) 4 pm (2)	Capsule inserted in mouth of 1 fish daily
Black-footed (Jackass) (*Spheniscus demersus*)	9.30 am (10)	9.30 am (4)	9.30 am (6)	9.30 am (2)	Capsule inserted in mouth of 1 fish daily
Adelie (*Pygoscelis adeliae*)	9.30 am (10) 4 pm (10)		9.30 am (6) 4 pm (6)	9.30 am (2) 4 pm (2)	Capsule inserted in mouth of 1 fish daily
Galapagos (*Spheniscus mendiculus*)	9.30 am (8) 4 pm (8)	9.30 am (6) 4 pm (6)		9.30 am (1) 4 pm (1)	Capsule inserted in mouth of 1 fish daily
Little Blue (*Eudyptula minor*)	9.30 am (4) 4 pm (4)	9.30 am (6) 4 pm (6)		9.30 am (1) 4 pm (1)	Capsule inserted in mouth of 1 fish daily

Struthioniformes

OSTRICH

The ostrich (*Struthio camelus*) is the largest of living birds. Although it is now found in the vast treeless and barren desert regions of Africa, until recent times it inhabited the Arabian peninsula. Today, ostriches are no longer found in wild flocks. They are being bred, on a large scale, on farms in South Africa for commercial feather production.

There is only one species, with most authorities recognizing four or five geographic races. For the most part, ostriches live in small parties of six or more in East and South Africa. Sometimes they gather in flocks of fifty or sixty, often in the company of grazing antelopes and zebras on reserves and national wildlife refuges. They feed on grass, shrubs, ground creepers, gourds and fallen wild figs. Small tortoises, lizards and insects are also eaten.

Adult males stand 2.4 to 3 m in height and may weigh as much as 157 kg. Males are black with white wing and tail plumes. Hens are brownish-grey in colour.

These flightless birds have large, powerful legs which enable them to run at speeds of up to 35 to 40 mph (65 kph). Excellent eyesight and acute hearing are their most important senses. Through an evolutionary process, the number of toes on each foot has been reduced to two.

The male ostrich is polygamous, mating with three or four hens to form a harem. When a territory is established, several hens may lay eggs in the same nest. The nest is a shallow depression in the sand in which seven to ten cream-coloured eggs are deposited. The eggs may measure 15 cm in length and 13 cm in diameter. One egg weighs about 1140 g—the equivalent of two dozen hen's eggs.

Both sexes incubate the eggs, and the incubation period is forty-two days. When first hatched, the chicks are dappled brown, with spots on neck and throat. The body feathers are stiff and straw-like in appearance and touch.

Ostriches are excellent parents, with both sexes sharing the duties of rearing the chicks. Insects must be abundant for the chicks when first hatched, as they can digest only insectivorous food and a small amount of vegetable matter for the first two or three weeks. Chicks grow rapidly and attain their full size in six to eight months, growing about 30 cm a month. Male birds mature at four years of age, the females a little earlier. The voice of the ostrich ranges from a loud hiss to a booming roar similar to that of a lion.

Hyenas, jackals, cheetahs, hunting dogs, lions and vultures are considered predators of ostrich eggs and chicks. In captivity, all adult birds are potentially dangerous. They can kick forward and kill a human easily with a single blow of their powerful legs and large feet.

Ostriches may live twenty to thirty years in captivity if well managed. All need large, spacious pens ranging from 0.5 to 36 hectares in size for successful propagation in captivity.

The feeding of ostriches and other ratites has undergone radical change in the last two decades. Balanced rations in pellet form are available in both Europe and the USA.

Daily Diet for Ostriches

Adult birds
*ZuPreem Ratite Diet: 450 g per 11 kg of body weight.
Chopped alfalfa (lucerne): 1 kg per bird.
Hydroponic greens (oats, barley): 4.6 kg per bird.
Oyster shell: free choice.

*For the constituents of all ZuPreem products, see Appendix I.

Young birds
a) Mix 4.6 kg ZuPreem Ratite Diet; 0.8 kg Trout Chow pellets; 2.3 kg Purina Rabbit Chow.
Feed this mixture at the rate of 1.8 g per 450 g of body weight, ad libitum, for the first two weeks.

b) After two weeks, continue feeding the same mixture ad libitum, plus a pan of 'hen-size' insoluble granite grit.

Note: Do not give oyster shell or any other calcium to the young birds as the above pellets contain ample calcium and phosphorus as well as protein and amino acids, vitamins and trace minerals.

Casuariiformes

Cassowaries

The Cassowary family, Casuariidae, has one genus, *Casuarius*, and three species (*C. bennetti*, *C. casuarius* and *C. unappendiculatus*). It is restricted to northern Australia, New Guinea and the adjacent islands. Cassowaries differ clearly from the ostriches and rheas in their structure and life. All are flightless and inhabit deep jungles. Their plumage is coarse and hair-like and is shiny black in the adult and rusty brown in the immature. Characteristic of most species is the large casque or bony helmet (10 cm) on the crown which protects the head as its bearer crashes through dense brushland and forests.

The bare skin of the head and neck is brilliantly coloured in adults: red, violet, orange, yellow or blue. Different species have one or two fleshy throat wattles. The body feathers are double-shafted with loose branches. The wing feathers consist of three to six wire-like wing quills, certainly an excellent example of degenerated wings through evolution. A green gland is absent.

The toes have stout claws, the inner toenail on each foot being as long as 13 cm, and these serve as powerful pointed weapons. Many Melanesian natives have lost an arm, leg or an entire stomach in hunting this bird. Propelled by its powerful legs and wedge-shaped body, a cassowary can plough through almost any type of vegetation (grassland, swamp or seemingly impenetrable jungles) at remarkable speeds. The body and wing feathers are still used by some New Guinea natives as currency.

Female cassowaries exceed the males in size and also have much longer wattles. Their height at the back varies from 1.2 to 1.7 m and weight from 25 to 75 kg. Cassowaries feed upon fruits and berries, supplemented by insects, grubs, snails, lizards, rodents and small mammals.

The pea-green eggs measure 190×88 mm and are laid in clutches of five to nine. The male incubates the eggs for fifty-four to fifty-six days and rears the chicks. When chicks are hatched, it may be necessary to separate the parent birds into adjoining pens. The chicks are taught to eat and feed from containers by the male bird.

We have given below a variety of food enjoyed by adult cassowaries.

Actually, adult birds are finicky eaters and about 1.4 kg of food is eaten daily, divided into two feedings. A good rule is to feed 450 g of food for each 23 kg of body weight in adult birds.

Cassowary chicks show little interest in feeding until six or seven days old. Mealworms, bread crumbs, diced tomatoes and bananas are good starting foods. Seven-day-old chicks will eat twenty-five mealworms, one after the other, refusing other food offered. In addition, chicks will take grit and chick-size oyster shells in separate feeding containers. The breeding of cassowaries is most difficult and challenges even breeders with many years of experience.

Insectivorous food is necessary for the first two weeks of the cassowary chick's life. At three weeks of age, they will taste and eat items listed below as growth continues. Birds should be fed four times daily as their appetite increases. Small mice or 'pinkies' are eaten eagerly by the male parent and the chicks when they are three weeks of age. Cassowary chicks grow slowly as compared to other ratite chicks.

The chicks are light red-brown in colour when hatched. The front of the neck is yellowish and there are three dark stripes down the body

Daily Diet for Adult and Chick Cassowaries

Food	Grams
Brown bread, 1-cm cubes	115
Bananas, 1-cm cubes	115
Tomatoes, 1-cm cubes	115
Eugenia berries, in season	115
Cotoneaster berries, in season	115
Pyracantha berries, in season	115
Raspberries, canned	115
Grapes, 1 cm in diameter	115
Raisins, soaked overnight in water	115
Apples, 1-cm cubes	115
Pears, 1-cm cubes	115
Figs, 1-cm cubes	115
Sweet potatoes, yams (cooked), 1 cm	115
Carrots, freshly ground	115
Quaker oatmeal	88
Purina Trout Chow	115
Bone meal	15
Calcium	15
Horse meat, finely ground	29
Mealworms—25	
Crickets—25	
Hydroponics (7-day oat grass)	115

feathers. As they grow, the chicks lose the feathers around their necks and the bare skin becomes blue. The feathers become darker as the bird matures and the black adult plumage is attained.

Yellow mealworms, larval stage of the common grain beetle, *Tenebrio molitor*, form an important supplement in the diet of the chicks. Mealworms are rich in living protein, amino acids, phosphorous compounds and Vitamins A and B, and provide the finest in natural food for birds.

Emu

The emu, *Dromaius novaehollandiae*, is a native of the open semi-arid plains of Australia. It is the only living member of its family. With the cassowary, it makes up the order Casuariiformes. The second largest of the world's flightless birds, it is grouped with the ratites—flightless running birds that have no keel on the breastbone. It is rapidly disappearing from many of its former haunts, hunted and persecuted because of the damage done to wheat crops in western Australia.

Emus stand 1.6 to 1.8 m and may weigh 36 to 45 kg. Females are usually smaller. Emus are difficult to sex accurately and several birds should be purchased at one time to form a breeding nucleus.

The grey-brown plumage is hairlike with double feathers, two separate feathers coming from the same quill. The feathers of the head and neck are black and curly. The skin of the face and neck is a rich blue in colour during the breeding season. The wings are rudimentary and primitive.

Emus have three toes and are fast runners, credited with speeds of 30 miles an hour (48 kph) for short distances. They can also swim well. These birds travel in flocks and family groups throughout the continent most of the year, forming pairs and establishing territories only in the breeding months of May to August, the coldest months of the year. The nesting season is usually in the spring when fresh grass and vegetation is 3 to 5 cm tall. This tender vegetation provides food for the newly hatched emu chicks.

Emus start to breed in their second year. For the nest, the emu makes a flat bed of grasses, twigs or leaves in open places, sometimes at the base of a tree or bush. The eggs are dark green in colour, avocado–like in appearance. Seven to eleven eggs make up the usual clutch. The egg measures 140×90 mm and weighs 700 g. The male alone incubates the eggs for a period of fifty-four to fifty-six days. He broods and rears the chicks until they are independent.

The chicks are sooty-white, strikingly patterned with black and tan stripes. Newly hatched chicks may weigh 400 to 450 g.

Both adults and chicks live largely on plant food, fruit and berries. They also eat many grasshoppers, praying mantis and caterpillars in season. Reliable records show emus living twenty-five to thirty years in good health. Many diets and formulas have been used for feeding emus in captivity. We have raised 850 chicks since 1937 using the following diets.

Daily Diet for Emu Chick

ZuPreem Brand Ratite Pellets (ground) and Rabbit Pellets mixed half and half, available at all times.

Whole wheat bread crumbs: ½ slice per chick.

Hard-boiled egg (including crumbled shell): 1 per chick.

Cottage cheese: 1 teaspoon per chick.

Chopped green food: alfalfa, kale, comfrey, hydroponic grass (oats, barley, wheat), celery leaves, parsley (cut fine with scissors) free choice.

Oyster shell, chick-size, in separate container; hen-size given when four weeks old.

Insects: crickets, grasshoppers, caterpillars: ten to thirty per bird at 7 am and 5 pm daily.

Water: in small rabbit crocks or pet food containers (top 13 cm; bottom 18 cm; height 9 cm).

Daily Diet for Adult Emu

Food	Protein (%)	Fat (%)	Calcium (%)	Ash (%)
154 g ZuPreem Ratite Diet*	21.0	3.5	2.5	10.0
154 g Purina Game Bird Layena	20.0	3.0	3.0	11.0
154 g Rabbit Pellets	16.0	2.5	0.91	7.3
(above items mixed equally)				
100 g chopped apple	0.3	0.4	12 mg	
21 g 1-cm bread cubes	4.2	2.6	18 mg	
18 g (2 tbs) boiled wheat	11.87	2.09	0.05	1.83
200 g fresh chopped alfalfa	18.6	2.3	1.47	10.9
or celery leaves				
or Hydroponic sprouted greens	12.6	4.6	0.056	22.8
7-day-old oats, wheat or barley				
Oyster shell (hen-size) ad libitum			85	

* 154 g ground meat may be used instead of ZuPreem Ratite.

[8]

Apterygiformes

KIWIS

New Zealand's curious forest birds, with a history of 8 million years, are three species of kiwis. They are the smallest members of the ratite group. It has been said that the Disneyesque Kiwis are the least birdlike of all birds. They are certainly among the most primitive. Nocturnal in habit, they hide during the day in rocky crevices and burrows. At night, they come out to feed on worms and insects. Kiwis are about the size of a hen, 44 to 60 cm in height, and they weigh from 1.8 to 2.7 kg.

They have thick hairlike feathers, no tail, long bills with the nostrils at the tip for locating food under the forest floor. Their short, strong legs are spaced far apart, and they run with an awkward rolling and noisy gait. Each leg has a sharp spur for use in defence against enemies. Their eyes are small and ratlike, with very poor vision in daylight. Completely flightless, they retain only remnants of wings and no feathers. Brown or greyish in colour, the sexes are similar, with the females usually larger than the males. The body feathers, with no interlocking barbules, shed easily when handled.

Kiwis nest in natural burrows under trees, laying one white egg that may weigh 450 g, a quarter of the body weight of an adult. The male incubates the single egg for a period of about seventy-five days. He hatches, broods and raises the chick without the assistance of the female.

Symbolic of its homeland and chief motif of the Dominion Seal, the Kiwi appears on New Zealand coins, pound notes and stamps and is used as a trademark for textiles, shoe polish, flour and a score of other products. It is highly protected.

There are three species of kiwis, the Brown, Little Spotted and Greater Spotted. The Brown Kiwi, *Apteryx australis*, stands 45 to 57 cm in height. There are three subspecies, the Southern, Northern and Stewart Island Brown Kiwis, *Apteryx australis australis*, *Apteryx a. mantelli* (North Island) and *Apteryx a. lawryi* (Stewart Island). The Little Spotted Kiwi, *Apteryx oweni*, stands 35 to 45 cm in height and is found in the western districts of South Island. The Greater Spotted Kiwi, *Apteryx haasti*, is 45 to 55 cm high and is also found in the western districts of South Island.

Today, kiwis live in wooded and bush areas of North Island, in the west of South Island and on Stewart Island, south of South Island.

Kiwis are rare in captivity. There are records of hatching in New Zealand and Australia, with laying and incubation recorded at the London Zoo, but data on nutrition remains fragmentary. In 1975, the National Zoo, Washington DC, established the first breeding record in North America with a North Island Kiwi, *Apteryx australis mantelli*.

Diet used by National Zoo, Washington DC

Earthworms, *Lumbricus terrestris* (night crawlers), are provided in the following manner. A worm box $91 \times 48 \times 30$ cm deep, with a screened bottom, is buried to within 75 mm of its top near the service door in the aviary, and the worm pan is placed within so escaping worms are confined. A second pan with fruit is provided daily. Blueberries, soaked raisins, diced fruit cocktail, strips of horse meat (worm-sized), soaked trout chow, chopped apples and oranges were placed in the pan. The food items were sprinkled with Squibbs Vionate, a multivitamin powder, and oyster shell flour. The consumption of fruit was consistent at 55 to 85 g per bird daily.

Earthworms were the preferred food, although the amount taken varied considerably each day. The National Zoo's chick was observed drinking water eight days after hatching. When ten days old, it was observed eating for the first time from a second feeding pan which contained earthworms plus a few mealworms sprinkled on top of the earthworms.

Diet used by Zoological Gardens of San Diego, California

The kiwi exhibit has 60 cm of mulch on the floor, consisting of oak leaf mould, sand and topsoil. This floor is seeded with 8 kg of fresh earthworms weekly, providing earthworms twenty-four hours daily.

The following are provided daily.
Earthworms (*Lumbricus terrestris*): 450 g.
Mealworms (*Tenebrio molitor*): 6 to 12 per bird, twice daily.
Whole wheat bread cubes: 8 per bird with 1 drop of wheat germ oil on each cube, twice daily.
Raisins (water-soaked overnight): 10 per bird.
Cotoneaster or pyracantha berries: 5 per day.
Grapes (in season): 4 or 5 per bird, diced into 6-mm pieces.
A piece of hydroponic (7-day) sprouted oats, barley or wheat.
Water, which is available at all times in a shallow 10-cm container 30×60 cm and large enough for bathing in.

Rheiformes

RHEAS

In the New World, the place of the Old World ostriches is taken by the rheas. They live in the grasslands and brushy regions of South America, where they are referred to as 'American Ostriches', 'Pampas Ostriches' and sometimes as 'Nandus' because of the male's peculiar courtship call. The rhea differs from the African Ostrich by the presence of three toes, a feathered neck and tarsal scutellations (scaling on the legs). Both the ostrich and rhea lack the aftershafts in their feathers. They are flightless, but have powerful legs which are adapted for strong running.

There are two species (each with three sub-species), the larger being the Greater Rhea, *Rhea americana*. It is found in the lowlands up to 1830 m in eastern and central Brazil, Paraguay, Uruguay, Bolivia and in central Argentina. This bird stands 0.9 to 1.2 m in height, and may weigh 20 to 25 kg when adult. Its general colour is slaty-grey with the feathers of the head black and the neck white, becoming dark between the shoulders. The under-body plumage is white with the exception of two black crescents on the upper breast. A white phase or colour mutation, sometimes pure white in colour, has been propagated in captivity. Those labinistic sports are now well established.

On the pampas, the Greater Rhea is said to associate with Pampas deer, just as the ostrich in Africa seeks the companionship of zebras and antelopes. The wing feathers are still collected annually by ranchers and the feathers are made into dusters and sold commercially in Brazil and Argentina.

On the pampas and in the open Andean highlands, these birds feed on grain, grass and other vegetable matter, supplemented with snails, lizards, snakes and insects. Rheas live in small bands, but occasionally as many as fifty are found together. Very wary, they quickly flee from danger. In the Greater Rhea, the eggs are yellow in colour when first laid. A normal clutch of eggs consists of six to ten eggs. The nest is made on the ground, in any depression available. Only the cock incubates the eggs and several hens may lay in the same nest. The eggs measure 135 × 95 mm and weigh 530 to 680 g. The normal incubation period is thirty-six to forty days.

The Darwin's Rhea (Lesser Rhea), *Pterocnemia pennata*, differs from the Greater Rhea in the following characteristics: smaller size, 90 cm in height; a shorter bill; legs feathered down to the knee joint; and brown body and wing feathers tipped with *white spots*. The eggs are pale green in colour, measuring 125×85 mm, and weigh 500 to 550 g. The colour provides a perfect camouflage when the eggs are deposited in patches of green grass.

Formerly abundant in southern Peru, Bolivia, north-west Argentina, in the Patagonian lowlands south to the Straits of Magellan, and in northern Chile, Darwin's Rheas have become scarce in recent years except in the far interior. They have now been placed on the endangered species list to save them from extinction.

The flightless rheas are comparatively easy to maintain in captivity. They may be kept in open pens surrounded with a 1.5-metre fence. They are prolific breeders. Rheas need not be kept in pairs as the cocks seldom fight among themselves in spacious pens. Six to eight individuals will live well together in a large pen. A cock will mate with three or four hens daily. Hens usually lay fertile eggs when two years of age. On large estates and ranches, various animals live well with rheas. A few shade trees or tall shrubs for shelter and privacy are desirable within large paddocks or pasture lands.

Over 1000 rheas, both Greater and Darwin's, have been raised successfully on the following diet.

From one to six weeks of age: Purina Game Bird Startena—free choice. After six weeks: Purina Game Bird F & M Chow.

Purina Game Bird Breeder Layena should be fed four weeks before the start of the laying season and continued until after the season ends. This food, plus oyster shell, should be available free choice. After the laying season, F & M Chow should be fed as a maintenance ration. Fresh alfalfa hay, finely chopped, or oat hydroponic grass which is seven days old, should be fed, free choice, sprinkled on the F & M Chow.

Our practice has been to feed adult rheas once a day, the earlier the better, and to give them sufficient food to ensure that some is left over to the following day. Food is fed in stainless steel pans. Water is provided in an open container 15 cm deep.

The chicks may be slow in learning to eat by themselves. They may be taught to pick from the food container or 280-ml rabbit water container by a 'trainer', a baby chick or day-old duckling placed in the brooder. It is not necessary for them to have free access to water until they are two weeks of age. If they show an inclination to drink before that time, water should be given early in the morning and the container then removed from the brooder. Many chicks drown in water containers.

Chicks usually start to feed when four to six days old. Cereals in pelleted form may be offered, free choice, when the chicks are two weeks old. Finely-cut green food, fresh alfalfa leaves, rape, chicory, sprouted oats or barley may be cut with a pair of scissors and sprinkled on the Startena or in the water container to induce the chicks to start eating. Rhea chicks should be offered fresh food and water at least three times daily. Food and water containers should be washed and cleaned between each feeding period.

Rhea chicks may grow 15 cm per month after the first four weeks. If the weather is warm, they thrive when released into a sheltered run where they can exercise and collect grit and fine gravel for roughage. Exercise is important for rapidly growing chicks.

A separate small pan of grit should be placed in the brooder or pen when the chicks start eating. This supplement accumulates in the gizzard or second stomach, where the food is ground or triturated.

Nutrient requirements for rheas are still not completely known. Further research is needed for more adequate diets. Information is being accumulated season after season in many collections.

Tinamiformes

TINAMOUS

Tinamous are primitive ground birds found from southern Mexico through Central and South America to Patagonia. There are forty species and all can fly, although poorly. They vary in size from 20 to 55 cm. All are protectively coloured in tawny browns with barred, streaked or mottled patterns. They have slender, weak bills and extremely short tails, sometimes covered by wing feathers. Their strong legs enable them to run well for short distances. The sexes are similar in colour and form, with some females larger than the males in size.

The tinamous are at home from steamy sea-level forests to the open pampas and into the high Andes to 4300 m. Some species sleep in trees in roosting territories, while others prefer the ground under protective vegetation. Tinamou behaviour may include the mating of one male with several females, or the mating of one female with several males. The females are aggressive and do much of the courting. Like most ratites, the male tinamou incubates the eggs, and broods and rears the chicks after they are hatched.

The females are good nesters and lay from two to ten eggs, usually on the ground under bushes or grasses or on the forest floor in beds of fallen leaves. Several hens may lay in the same nest and leave the incubation to the male. If floods or predators destroy a clutch of eggs, the male will call new hens into his territory who then supply him with another clutch of eggs. Incubation periods range from seventeen to twenty-two days, sometimes more.

The eggs of tinamous are said to be the most beautiful in the world. They come in many colours—vivid green, turquoise blue, purple, wine-red, chocolate, buff and yellow—all enhanced by a highly polished, glazed porcelain appearance.

These birds feed on seeds and small fruits which they pick from the ground or from plants. They also eat opening buds, tender leaves, blossoms and even roots. Half of their diet consists of insects and their larvae, worms and molluscs. They may swallow small rodents whole; the larger ones they shake and beat against the ground until broken into smaller pieces.

Tinamous are hunted widely throughout South America for both sport and food. The breast meat is light in colour like that of a chicken and has a sweet, gamey taste. A number of efforts have been made to introduce tinamous as game birds into North America for sporting purposes, but these have met with little success. The birds will not thrive near populated areas or traffic-infested highways; nor can they reproduce fast enough to compete with modern firearms.

Captive management and propagation is limited today. Only a handful of the forty species have reproduced well in captivity. Unfortunately, tinamou chicks remain difficult to rear successfully.

Daily Diet for Adult Tinamous

Seeds (1 container, thoroughly mixed): $\frac{1}{3}$ canary seed; $\frac{1}{3}$ millet; $\frac{1}{3}$ milo.
Oyster shell (hen-size): free choice.
Fruit (in a separate container): cotoneaster berries, pyracantha berries, eugenia berries, or blue-berries—6 per bird, daily.
Greens: hydroponics (7-day, sprouted grain) 13-cm square piece fed in shaded area; comfrey leaves—2 per bird, twice daily.
Insects: mealworms—10 per bird, twice daily; crickets—10 per bird.
Hard-boiled egg: crumbled, including shell, on top of berries in fruit container.

Daily Diet for Tinamou Chicks (in Brooder)

Purina Trout Chow: small, crumbled.
Quaker Oats: $\frac{1}{2}$ tsp per chick, sprinkled on Trout Chow.
Mealworms: 3 or 4 per chick, dropped on Trout Chow 2 or 3 at a time. In this way, they learn to eat the crumbles as they go after the live food.
Twelve mealworms may be eaten daily per chick, divided into four feedings.
Hard-boiled egg: including shell, crumbled finely and fed in separate container, 10 cm in diameter and 1.3 cm deep.
Chickweed, dandelion leaves or comfrey leaves tied in small bundles and dangled on a string or fine wire low enough nearly to touch the floor in order that chicks can tear the leaves off.

Note: Chicks usually refuse to start feeding after hatching without the aid of their parents. Baby chicks or quail do not work as trainers or companions since tinamou chicks are timid and aloof in competitive feeding. The chicks simply dehydrate and starve to death with abundant food and water in front of them.

Remedy: The chicks must be fed by hand with a syringe or eye-dropper three or four times a day for a period of two weeks. During the first week each chick must be caught and hand fed with a syringe. In the second week, they learn to drink the soupy-like mixture voluntarily from the tip of the syringe. By the third week, the chicks will readily eat Trout Chow pellets, mealworms, hard-boiled eggs and green food dangled in front of them.

Tinamou Chick Formula to use in Syringe

Measurements by volume, not by weight. Use standard measuring cup and spoon.

$\frac{1}{2}$ cup Sperry Wheat Heart Cereal (or Gerber High Protein Baby Cereal, or Farex).
$\frac{1}{8}$ teaspoon salt.
$\frac{1}{2}$ teaspoon fine cuttlefish bone.
1 teaspoon Karo corn syrup (or golden syrup).
2 fresh egg yolks.
Milk or water added to make soup consistency.
4 drops ABDEC vitamin supplement.

Mix dry ingredients, add syrup and egg yolk, then milk or water to make a soup-like mixture, boil over low heat for 3 to 5 minutes, stirring gently. Cool until finger warm, add 4 drops of vitamin, stir in. Feed in syringe.

Pelecaniformes

PELICANS · CORMORANTS · ANHINGAS

Pelicans

Pelicans are the largest members of this group. There are six species—two in the New World and four in the Old. Pelicans have been known so long that the very derivation of their name is lost in antiquity. All are aquatic, fish-eating birds with all four toes connected by webs.

One species is brown, the others white with black wingtips. Their common names (White, Brown, Red-backed) illustrate the colour of their plumage. Some have orange, red or yellow colours on the bill, pouch and bare part of the face. The length is 1.6 to 1.8 m and the wingspan 1.8 to 2.8 m. The weight ranges from 3.6 to 7.2 kg.

The large gular pouch, which can hold 14 litres of water, is used as a dip net in catching prey. The fish are not stored in the pouch but the water is strained out and the fish are swallowed. Only the brown pelican dives for fish while flying. All others catch their prey while swimming on the surface of the water.

Although powerful fliers and good swimmers, pelicans are clumsy and slow on land, since their feet are positioned far back to make for more efficiency in swimming. They sometimes have trouble becoming airborne and on windless days have to run, flapping, a considerable distance over land or water to take off.

Sociable birds, they roost and nest in colonies, even out of the breeding season. The colony may be close to either fresh or salt water. The nests are usually mere hollows scraped in the ground, on ledges or in low bushes on off-shore islands. Two to three bluish-white or yellowish eggs form a clutch. The incubation period varies from thirty to forty-two days. The chicks are helpless, blind and naked when hatched. Chicks are fed predigested fish which the young take out of the throat pouches or the throats of the adults.

The white or brownish-black down plumage appears only after eight to fourteen days. The fledgeling period lasts twelve to fifteen weeks. The young become sexually mature when three to four years of age. Sexes are difficult to determine. Females may have shorter beaks and may be smaller in size.

Fishermen dislike pelicans because the pouch-net which they carry under the great beak is large and the appetite for fish is great. However, research has determined that pelicans feed mainly on fish which are unsuitable for human consumption.

Pelicans in captivity live very well on a diet of fish, varied occasionally with a little raw meat. They usually become quite tame. They live well on a large lake and if there is a small island in the middle of the lake on which they can rest undisturbed there is a chance they may breed, although pelicans have not propagated well in captivity. Pelicans do not live well in small pens as small quarters are impossible to keep clean and dirty soil will have a very unpleasant odour. Individuals have lived forty years in well managed collections.

Diet for Pelicans (1.8 kg Daily per Bird)

230 g Pacific Mackerel (*Pneumatophorus diego*)*.
230 g Jack Mackerel (*Trachurus symmetricus*).
230 g Mullet (*Mugil cephalus*).
17 cm Pacific Herring (*Clupea pallasii*)*.
17 cm Sardine (*Sardinops caerulea*).
17 cm Northern Anchovy (*Engraulis mordax*).
17 cm Surf Smelt (*Hypomesus pretiosis*)*.
17 cm Top (Bay) Smelt (*Atherinops affinis*).
17 cm Grunion (*Leuresthes tenuis*).
23 cm Whitebait (*Allosmerus allenuatus*)*.
21 cm Queenfish (*Seriphus politus*).
25 cm Squid (*Lollinguncula brevis*)*.
Horsemeat*—2.5 cm pieces.

*Favourite food, purchased in season.

Cormorants

Cormorants or shags are fish-eating birds common along the coasts, offshore islands and inland fresh water lakes. There are twenty-nine species which inhabit both the Eastern and Western hemispheres. They range in size from the Pygmy Cormorant, *Phalacrocorax niger* (45.5 to 50 cm), of the Middle East and southern Europe, up to the Common (Great) Cormorant, *Phalacrocorax carbo* (101 cm), which is almost cosmopolitan in distribution.

All are long-bodied, comparatively long-necked, with short legs at the end of the body and a bill which is hooked strongly at the tip. All of the cormorants catch fish by diving from the surface and chasing them underwater. They seldom eat the fish underwater, but come to the surface and juggle them around in the beak to position them before swallowing. In Japan, trained cormorants, Temminck's Cormorant (*Phalacrocorax capillatus*), are tethered from fishing boats, with a tight collar to keep them from swallowing the fish. The birds are released into schools of fish and they bring the captured fish back to the fishing boats.

Cormorants resemble geese when flying, and loons when in the water. Most are black or dark in colour with a greenish or bluish sheen to the feathers. In some, under-parts are white.

Although they feed mostly on fish unfit for human consumption, crabs, squid and amphibian larvae are also eaten. Many commercial fishermen kill them on sight. Small eels are a favourite food in bays. Rock cod, carp and other slow-swimming fish form the bulk of their diet. The faster fish escape them.

Most of these birds breed in sizeable colonies on rocky islets, sea cliffs and occasionally in trees. The Flightless Cormorant (*Nannopterum harrisi*) of the Galapagos Islands has lost its power of flight through degeneration of the wing feathers and is forced to nest on the ground. It is certainly the most primitive of the group.

Flimsy nests are constructed of sticks, grass and vegetation, plastered together with their droppings and offal. Two to four eggs, pale blue or green, are laid each season. Both sexes incubate the eggs, brood and feed the chicks. The incubation period is three to four weeks. The young are hatched naked, but are soon covered with black down. They grow rapidly and when two months old can fly and leave the nest. The parents continue to feed them until they begin to catch prey by themselves.

The social life of cormorants and their social ceremonies are varied. Much has been learned about the social behaviour of social animals from the general principles of behaviour that were discovered in the study of cormorants.

In captivity, these birds may live fifteen to eighteen years in large enclosures or on lakes with pelicans and other marine birds. They should not be kept with breeding waterfowl as they have been known to catch and eat both birds and small mammals.

Diet for Cormorants and Shags (1.8 kg Daily per Bird)

Choice of the following fish, divided into 8.00 am and 6.00 pm feedings.
18–20 cm Northern Anchovy (*Engraulis mordax*).
18 cm Pacific Herring (*Clupea pallasii*).
18 cm Top (Bay) Smelt (*Antherinops affinis*).
20 cm Whitebait (*Allosmerus allenuatus*).
20 cm Sardine (*Sardinops caerulea*).

Anhingas

The anhingas, snakebirds or darters are closely allied to the cormorants and somewhat resemble them. They are long, slim birds with elongated, snake-like necks and sharp thin bills that render underwater spear-fishing a simple matter. Anhingas hunt for their prey under water, feeding on fish, frogs, snakes and insects. As these birds swim, only their heads rise above the surface and they look very much like water snakes. Large fish and water snakes are brought to the surface and flung into the air so that they can be swallowed head first.

Since the long tail, wing and body feathers become thoroughly saturated while the birds are swimming, they must climb out of the water and seek a resting place in the sunlight in order to dry their feathers before flight is possible. The toes of the stout webbed feet terminate in sharp claws which enable the bird to climb with ease.

There are four species, one in the New World, the American Anhinga, *Anhinga anhinga*, and three Old World species of the Rufous Anhinga, *Anhinga rufa*, with races in Africa, Asia and the Philippine Islands.

Anhingas inhabit lakes, rivers and swamps in tropical areas and are never found far from water. In the air, they soar and glide like the pelicans, following slow-moving rivers and fresh water lakes inland. Often they nest in colonies with herons and ibises, although sometimes they may be seen in communities of forty to sixty birds in a group of trees with no other water birds near.

Each of the four species show white or buff streaks and spots on the back and wings. The body plumage is black or brown according to the species.

Nests are usually made in low trees or bushes near water. They are constructed of sticks, leaves, dry grass, roots and moss. Both sexes participate in carrying material to the nest site, which is usually chosen by the male. Two to five eggs, bluish or dark greenish-white are laid. The eggs are incubated by both sexes for twenty-five to twenty-eight days and both brood and feed the young. Nestlings are hatched naked and blind, but a coat of white down soon appears. Crayfish, salamanders, frogs and water insects are fed to the chicks, as well as small fish. The young stay in the nest or near it until they are fledged at the age of six to eight weeks.

Anhingas live well in captivity on a diet of small fish and frogs. They need warmth and protection in cold climates as they must be considered tropical or semi-tropical birds. I know of no record of a successful breeding in captivity.

Daily Diet for Anhingas

12.5 cm Whitebait fish (*Allosmerus allenuatus*) or Anchovy (*Engraulis mordax*).

5–10 cm Leopard frog (*Rana pipiens*) (or *R. esculenta*, *R. temporaria*, *R. ridibunda*).

20 fish daily per bird, half fed in the morning, half in the evening.

10 frogs daily per bird, half in morning and half in evening.

Ciconiiformes

HERONS · IBISES · SPOONBILLS · STORKS

Members of this order are primarily wading birds with long legs and long bills. Some are fishers while others feed on small rats, mice, mammals, crabs, crayfish, snakes, frogs, insects and even carrion.

Herons

Herons and their allies live along quiet streams, reedy marshes, shallow bays, on islands and near ponds and rivers all around the world. There are sixty-three species. They live in both tropical and temperate regions.

Members of this family vary greatly in size. The largest, the Goliath Heron, *Ardea goliath*, of Africa, stands 1.5 m in height and weighs 2.2 to 2.7 kg. The smallest, the Least Bittern, *Ixobrychus exilis*, of North America, is only 25 cm in height and weighs 1.6 kg. In colour, they range from snow white to the concealing shades of brown, blue and grey.

Although most bills are long and pointed, a few have the bill widened, spoon-shaped or boat-shaped in appearance. Many have crests or ornamental plumes, especially during the breeding season. These birds fly with necks drawn in and legs extended. All have broad, rounded wings and four long, spreading toes. In some species, the front three toes are slightly webbed at the base. The middle claw has a serrated edge which is used as a comb in cleaning the plumage. Herons possess patches of powder down on the breast, at the sides of the rump and in the groin (not in all species) used to dress the feathers. Powder downs are feathers that crumble at the tip to form powder which is rubbed into the plumage with the bill and comblike claw. Thus the plumage is kept water-repellant and the remains of fish grease are removed from the feathers.

Herons stalk their prey carefully or stand and wait for it, their long slender necks in a resting position, drawn back into an 'S' shape. Bitterns depend on their long strong toes to climb about in the reed beds to capture frogs and large insects.

Most herons breed in colonies and roost in communal flocks out of the nesting season. The nests are built in trees, shrubs or reeds, on rocks or on the ground (in the Galapagos Islands). Usually both parents build the nest and relieve each other during the incubation period. The clutch consists of three to five eggs, but the smallest bittern lays as many as nine eggs. The eggs are white, greenish, blue, olive-brown, and a few are spotted.

The incubation period ranges from sixteen days (bitterns) to twenty-five or twenty-eight days in the larger herons. Both sexes feed the young by regurgitation as the chicks grasp the parents' beaks crosswise. Chicks grow rapidly with abundant food and are usually fully fledged at the age of two months. Herons mature at the age of two years and will breed successfully at that age.

Many herons live well in captivity. The longevity record seems to be twenty-four years. Herons are beneficial to man and agriculture. They catch rats, mice and countless water insects which are destructive to fish.

Diets for Herons (Twice Daily)

Species	Fish (mackerel, anchovy)		Mice (g)	Meat (g)	Total Feeding grams
	No.	Weight (g)			
Goliath Heron (*Ardea goliath*)	2	450	40	120	610
Great Blue Heron (*Ardea herodias*)	6	1350	40	120	1510
Black-crowned Night Heron (*Nycticorax nycticorax*)	3	675		120	795
Great White Heron (*Ardea occidentalis*)	6	1350	40	120	1510
Little Blue Heron (*Egretta caerulea*)	3	675		120	795
Common (Great White) Egret (*Egretta alba*)	3	675		120	795
Cattle Egret (*Bubulcus ibis*)	3	675		120	795
Snowy Egret (*Egretta thula*)	3	675		120	795
Boat-billed Heron (*Cochlearius cochlearius*)	3	675	40	120	835
Tiger Bittern (Rufescent Tiger-Heron) (*Tigrisoma lineatum*)	6	1350	40	120	1510

Note : Fish and ground horse meat are fed in separate stainless steel pans, 60 × 30 × 50 cm. Water is added to prevent food from drying out.

In breeding colonies around lakes, masses of faecal matter, rotting eggs and dead chicks and adults fall into the water. This material supplies food for plankton, the basis of food for all young fish.

These birds require large aviaries or flight cages with a pool and trees for perching high above the ground. They will not mix well with birds smaller than themselves and should not be placed with breeding pheasants or ducks as they certainly will eat small chicks and ducklings when hungry. Small bitterns do not live well in captivity as three-quarters of their diet consists of insects. We recommend that orphaned bitterns be released into the wild as soon as they are fledged and are independent of hand-feeding.

Ibises and Spoonbills

Twenty-eight species of ibis and spoonbill inhabit the warm and tropical countries around the world and they are easily separated by their bills. Ibises have long, slender, downward-curving bills. Spoonbills have broad, spoon-shaped bills at the tip, 50 to 95 cm in length. They are all sociable and breed in large colonies. They wander or migrate in troops.

Ibises fly with their necks straight out in front, their long legs trailing behind. They are fresh-water birds and probe the mud and water for small fish, frogs, crayfish, insects and snakes. In Australia and Egypt their feeding habits make them valuable to farmers since they eat the grasshoppers and locusts injurious to crops. Often they follow the plough and feed on the grubs and other insects which are turned up in the furrows.

There are many different colours in the plumage of this group. Many ibises are white. The White-faced Glossy Ibis (*Plegadis chihi*) is a uniform bronze brown with a metallic sheen. The Scarlet Ibis (*Eudocimus ruber*) is a spectacular red. The plumage of all spoonbills is white with the exception of the Roseate Spoonbill (*Platalea ajaja*), which has pink or red wings, tail and under-parts. The beautiful pink feathers which were collected for making fans, and the bills which were inlaid with silver and sold commercially in Florida, almost exterminated this species. Protective legislation and the establishment of refuges has stopped this persecution. Today, a small remnant has survived of the former thousands that at one time lived in Florida.

The ibis was treated as a sacred, holy bird in ancient Egypt. This was probably due to its appearance each year at the time when the Nile River began to rise. Farming was determined by the arrival of great flocks of

Diet for Ibis and Spoonbill (Each Feeding)

Species	Roxanthin Red Colour Supplement/Carophyll Red (g)	Fish (g)	Meat (g)	Total grams
Scarlet Ibis (*Eudocimus ruber*)	6	60	120	186
White Ibis (*Eudocimus albus*)		60	120	180
White-faced Glossy Ibis (*Plegadis chihi*)		60	120	180
Sacred Ibis (*Threskiornis aethiopicus*)		60	120	180
Australian White Ibis (*Threskiornis molucca*)		60	120	180
Straw-necked Ibis (*Threskiornis spinicollis*)		60	120	180
Black-headed (Oriental) Ibis (*Threskiornis melanocephala*)		60	120	180
Roseate Spoonbill (*Platalea ajaja*)	6	60	120	186
Yellow-billed Spoonbill (*Platalea flavipes*)		60	120	180
African Spoonbill (*Platalea alba*)		60	120	180
White Spoonbill (*Platalea leucorodia*)		60	120	180

Note: Ibises and spoonbills are fed twice daily at 7.00 am and 4.00 pm.

ibises which controlled the insect pests so injurious to the crops. The Egyptians made the Sacred Ibis an integral part of their religion and their hieroglyphics. To them, the ibis was the god Thoth.

The nests of ibises are circular, made of sticks, leaves and herbage which is added to give the nest substance. Nests may be constructed in trees, bushes, or on the ground. Three to five eggs are laid, white or pale blue. They may be plain or irregularly spotted or streaked with brown. Both sexes incubate the eggs from twenty-one to twenty-five days. The chicks are covered with black down and are fed by regurgitation by the parent birds. The young are fed crayfish, insects, fish roe, grasshoppers, cutworms, slugs and snails for the first two weeks. The young are fledged and leave the nest when six to eight weeks old. The immature grey-brown plumage does not change to white until the second year.

Spoonbills prefer to build nests in trees, bushes, shrubs or trampled-down reeds which hang over water marshes. Three or four chalk-white eggs, freckled with yellowish or reddish brown, are laid. The incubation period is twenty-one to twenty-three days and is shared by both parents. The young remain in the nest about eight weeks. Then they leave the nest but follow the parents who continue to feed them.

Storks

There are seventeen species of storks found from temperate Eurasia through Africa, northern Australia, India, Indonesia, and North and South America. In size they range from 50 to 150 cm in height. The wings are long and broad, the tail short and usually rounded. The body is heavy, the neck long, the bill large and variously shaped. The front toes are partly webbed. The face or head is bare in some species. Some are black and white, others are grey and some are all black or all white. The sexes look alike although the female is usually smaller in size. Some species migrate and fly strongly with neck out straight. They soar well and often.

The courtship dance is spectacular. Voiceless, they rattle the bill like castinets. Their nests consist of stick platforms on trees, low shrubs, cliff ledges, chimneys or buildings. Three to five chalky-white eggs are laid annually. The incubation period in the European White Stork (*Ciconia ciconia*) is thirty-eight or thirty-nine days. Both sexes incubate the eggs and feed the chicks.

Storks are devoted parents and bring all kinds of food to the nest for their young. The chicks are fed earthworms, grubs, newly hatched grass-hoppers, mice, frogs, snakes, lizards, ground squirrels, beetles, fish and carrion (marabou stork) may all be part of their diet.

The young are able to fly at the age of two months. Storks mature very slowly and do not become sexually mature until four or five years of age. The storks of Europe migrate to South Africa for the winter, returning to their nesting places with the coming of spring.

The Greater Adjutant Stork (*Leptoptilos dubius*) of India and the Marabou Stork (*Leptoptilos crumeniferus*) of Africa are carrion-eating. The Shoebill (Whale-headed) Stork (*Balaeniceps rex*) of central Africa feeds on river fish, frogs and snails. The small black and white Abdim's (White-bellied) Stork (*Ciconia abdimii*) found in the Sudan and South Africa feeds mainly on insects, army-worms (larvae of moths), locusts, rhinoceros beetles and large larvae from compost piles. The African Saddlebill Stork (*Ephippiorhynchus senegalensis*) must be the most beautiful of the group—with its colourful yellow saddle plate on a red and black bill. It feeds on frogs and fish from the swamps and along lakes from Ethiopia and Senegal to South Africa.

In the New World, there are three storks. The American Wood Stork (*Mycteria americana*) is a large white bird with black wings and tail, which ranges from southern Florida to Peru and Argentina. The Jabiru Stork (*Jabiru mycteria*) is also black and white, with a bald head. It ranges from southern Mexico to Argentina. The Maguari Stork (*Euxenura maguari*) is found along streams from the Guianas to southern Argentina. All feed on frogs, toads, snakes, insects, fish and any other small creatures they encounter in marshes and swamps.

Storks and other large birds of this type are usually not desirable for amateur aviculturists. Eight species must be considered as either threatened or endangered at this time and captive propagation should be encouraged.

Diet for Storks (Each Feeding)

Species	Fish (g)	Meat (g)	Mice (g)	Purina Game Bird Breeder Layena (g)
European White Stork (*Ciconia ciconia*)	120	240	60	240
Abdim's (White-bellied) Stork (*Ciconia abdimii*)	60	240	60	240
Greater Adjutant Stork (*Leptoptilos dubius*)	120	240	60	240
Marabou Stork (*Leptoptilos crumeniferus*)	120	240	60	240
Shoebill (Whale-headed) Stork (*Balaeniceps rex*)	120	240	60	240
African Saddlebill Stork (*Ephippiorhynchus senegalensis*)	120	240	60	240
American Wood Stork (*Mycteria americana*)	120	240	60	240
Jabiru Stork (*Jabiru mycteria*)	120	240	60	240
Maguari Stork (*Euxenura maguari*)	120	240	60	240

Note : Birds are fed twice daily. Mix Purina Bird Breeder Layena with ground meat. 1/1 as basic mixture.

Phoenicopteriformes

FLAMINGOS

Flamingos hold a prominent place among the most beautiful and graceful birds. They live in many parts of the world; Africa, India, southern Europe, the Caribbean coasts, the Andean highlands, and the Galapagos Islands. Six species are recognized, two in the Old World, the Greater Flamingo (*Phoenicopterus ruber roseus*) and the Lesser Flamingo (*Phoenicconaias minor*) of Africa. In the New World, the Caribbean Flamingo (*Phoenicopterus ruber ruber*), introduced into Florida, the Chilean Flamingo (*Phoenicopterus ruber chilensis*), the Andean Flamingo (*Phoenicoparrus andinus*) and the James Flamingo (*Phoenicoparrus jamesi*) live in shallow lagoons, lakes, estuaries of fresh, brackish and salt water.

All are wading birds with long legs and necks. The bills are specialized, bent in the middle. The tongue and bill bear comb-like filaments that act as strainers for the minute particles upon which flamingos feed. Diatoms, blue-green algae, molluscs, crustaceans, insects and small fish are drawn into the mouth by a built-in pump, sieved and then swallowed.

Sexes are alike in colour, the female usually smaller than the male in height. Most flamingos attain their adult plumage at the age of two or three years. Five- and six-year-old birds become breeding birds. The breeding season is about six weeks long. The birds nest in colonies in hundreds or even thousands, close together, and always near water. The nests are made of mud in the shape of the base of a cone, with a shallow depression in the centre for the egg. One chalky-white egg is laid. Both sexes participate in building the nest, using materials such as mud, stones, grasses and feathers. The incubation period is thirty days. Males and females alternate in incubating the eggs. Both parents feed the chick by regurgitating partially-digested food. The chick is covered with white down when first hatched and can swim when seven or eight days of age.

At this early age the bill is straight and the legs and feet are red. When ten days old the chick sometimes leaves the nest to explore its new world. It is followed and guarded closely by the parents. When six months old, the young are able to fly and accompany the parents to different feeding grounds.

In captivity, flamingos have lived well for over forty years. Four of the six species have raised chicks in North American and European collections.

Good nutritional diets have been developed in recent years which have improved maintenance and reproduction. For many years, flamingos in captivity would lose their brilliant colouration due to unbalanced and unsuitable diets. Today, with the help of science and professional nutritionists, supplements have been developed which when added to the diet are not only successful in retaining the natural colour, but also in restoring colour to plumage which has already faded.

Flamingos were first raised in North America at the Hialeah Race Track in Florida in 1942. Cooked rice, dried shrimp (ground), dog biscuits and cod liver oil were used in that collection for many years, with fifty to seventy-five chicks being produced annually.

Flamingo Diet No. 1: Quantity Consumed Daily per Adult Bird

28 g cooked brown rice.
28 g fresh carrot pulp (ground).
57 g Purina kibbled dog food.
28 g fresh ground shrimp.
28 g fresh ground meat.
28 g ground spiny lobster shell.
57 g brown bread.
6 g Roxanthin Red 10 (dry canthanaxthin) (Carophyll Red) or Caradee (vitamin A, B, carrot oil).
28 g table salt.

All ingredients are thoroughly mixed in an electric blender and then fed in stainless steel pans.

Flamingo Diet No. 2 (used at Zoologisk Have, Copenhagen, Denmark)

4.5 kg commercial waterfowl and pheasant pellets.
4.0 g dried shrimp shell.
2.0 g alfalfa (lucerne) meal.
120 g paprika (capsicum).

Finely ground ingredients are mixed with water to form a thick gruel which flamingos take from feeding troughs.

Flamingo Diet No. 3: daily ration per adult bird

28 g ground meat.
57 g Game Bird Breeder Layena.

28 g boiled rice.
28 g ground shrimp.
28 g trout pellets.
57 g wheat bread.
28 g ground carrots.
113 g Premix.

Premix

227 g paprika powder (capsicum).
9 g Roxanthin Red 10 (or Carophyll Red).
57 g Vitamycin (or Cytacon, Belfortiss Elixir or Albevita).
15 g manganese sulphate.
85 g salt, trace mineralized.
153 g dehydrated alfalfa meal.

Thoroughly mix dry ingredients and add to basic diet in blender before feeding.

Note: 170 g of carotene rich dietary grass may be used in place of premix as a source of B carotenoids (*International Zoo Yearbook*, Vol. 15, 1975: Fox, Dennis L., Lint, K. C.)

Anseriformes

SWANS · GEESE · DUCKS · SCREAMERS

Waterfowl give many hours of satisfying recreation to millions of people in thousands of private collections and exhibits in parks and zoological gardens. Numerous species of waterfowl from the four corners of the globe are gathered together by waterfowl breeders and displayed for study and enjoyment. They are among the most colourful birds in the world. They are easily maintained and their tameness allows one to explore their behaviour intimately. The name 'waterfowl' has come to refer to the family Anatidae, which is composed of 144 species.

Waterfowl are world-wide in distribution except for the polar regions. They live in varied habitats, usually near water. Most species are migratory, flying strongly and rapidly. Except during the breeding season when they separate for nesting, they may be seen flying or feeding in flocks of hundreds or thousands. They are mainly vegetarian, although some forms eat fish, eels, crustaceans, molluscs and aquatic insectivorous food.

Size varies within the groups. In general, swans are the largest, geese are second in size and ducks are the smallest of the Order. They range from 28 to 170 cm in length and from 310 to 13,500 g in weight. Although diversified in form, size and colour, all members are swimming birds with comparatively short legs. The three front toes are webbed or partly webbed. The wings are narrow and pointed and tails are usually short. Necks are medium long.

Bills are flat, wide and rounded at the end. The plumage is dense and underlaid with down which is used to line the nest during the nesting season. The feathers of the body, wings and head are waterproofed by oil from a gland located at the base of the tail. This oil is worked into the feathers by the bill. Some species are alike in sexual appearance.

The nests are made from many materials: sticks, weeds, reeds, grasses and leaves. They are usually formed into mounds rising a foot or so above the marsh level. Some are built on islands. Others are found in tree holes or in deserted crow or squirrel nests in trees. The eggs number from two to twenty, and are white or pale green in colour and unspotted. Incubation ranges from twenty-one to thirty-eight days. The young are hatched with thick downy feathers and are able to run about, swim and follow their parents a day or two after hatching.

[31]

With 144 species and 247 races of swans, geese and ducks, we will give diets only for the groupings under which they are classified.

Swans

The nine species of the genera *Cygnus* and *Coscoroba* are distributed all over the world with the exception of the continent of Africa. Aloof and wary, swans are the undisputed monarchs of the air. They nest around the polar ice, flying to temperate zones in winter, choosing remote and uninhabited places where they scatter to rest and feed.

Wild swans far outnumber the semi-domesticated mute swans which are seen on park lakes and rivers around the world. The wild birds nest in uninhabited areas and fly so high on migration that the faint measured beat of their wings and the bugle-clear notes of their call as they pass are the only indication of their presence.

Six species are pure white birds from the high latitudes of the northern hemisphere. These are: Whooper (*Cygnus cygnus cygnus*); Bewick's (*Cygnus columbianus bewickii*); Jankowski's (*Cygnus columbianus jankowskii*); Mute (*Cygnus olor*); Trumpeter (*Cygnus cygnus buccinator*); and Whistling (*Cygnus columbianus columbianus*). Three live in the southern hemisphere: the Black-necked (*Cygnus melancoryphus*) and the white Coscoroba (*Coscoroba coscoroba*) of southern South America and the Black Swan (*Cygnus atratus*) of Australia and Tasmania, which has been introduced into New Zealand.

Swans are most ornamental and interesting. They may be raised on lakes, on small ponds, or in pens with protected water and adequate vegetation. They live and breed on water. Swans mature at the age of three years and may live twenty to thirty years in captivity. Most experienced breeders can sex young birds accurately.

The importance of good nutrition cannot be emphasized too strongly. On ponds and lakes there should be an abundance of duck weed, water hyacinths and other water weeds. The birds will prune them, eating the roots where they are thick and nibble the tips above water. Plant rushes, reeds, wild celery, cat-tails or other ornamental plants should be placed around the pond or lake to provide windbreaks and privacy as well as for food.

For a good basic diet it is necessary to provide added green food when pairs are kept in pens. A feeding pool should be provided, as the swan's bill is not adapted for taking greens from dry ground. Grass clippings are a good substitute for water plants as they contain vitamins and minerals. Lettuce, celery and cabbage trimmings may be collected from food markets, but care should be taken to see that no plastic materials, bottle caps or sour milk have contaminated the greens. Such greens provide roughage and bulk, but should be used as a supplement and not as the basic diet. Swans live and breed on a balance of greens and grain foods in captivity.

Fresh succulent grass is nature's most perfectly balanced food for many birds. In the early stages it contains most of the known vitamins and minerals necessary for health, plus an abundance of the still little known but vitally necessary enzymes, hormones and 'grass juice factors'. All of these nutrients are in balance as nature intended when grass is fed to rheas, waterfowl and gallinaceous birds.

Daily Diet for Swans

Pond weed (*Elodea canadensis*): natural food in ponds and lakes.
Hydroponic grass (7-day sprouted barley, oats or wheat): 1 to 1.5% of body weight per bird.
Lettuce, grass clippings, celery.
Bread: 1 slice per bird.
Purina Pullet Developer or Checkerettes: fed in containers placed 1 m off the ground.
1 hard-boiled egg (including shell, crumbled) sprinkled on Developer Checkerettes for cygnets or young after four days of age.

Geese

Geese are migratory waterfowl and highly social. They usually have large heads and thick necks, long legs set forward and small feet adapted for walking on land where they gather most of their food by grazing. The bill is strong and narrow with serrations, called 'teeth', on the sides. The lores are feathered. Wings are long and sharp and some have a bony knob or spur at the bend. The tail is fairly long and rounded, composed of sixteen to twenty feathers. Colours are brown, grey and white, and the pattern is usually modest or plain.

All of the geese are very similar in their life habits. They fly and walk with ease and for the most part feed on land. They eat grass, leaves, berries and seeds. They sometimes cause damage to crops on their winter range.

When grazing in wheat and barley fields, they use the teeth of the mandibles to great advantage, cutting the newly-planted green food with the sides of the bill. Except during the breeding season, they congregate in flocks and migrate in regular formation. While feeding, one bird is selected as a lookout to warn the flock of danger. The nights are spent on banks and flats or among reeds on lakes, marshes, rivers or estuaries. The birds fly to the fields and plains in the early morning. After feeding, they return to the water to drink and rest in the middle of the day, flying out to their feeding grounds again in the early afternoon and remaining until dusk. Geese swim well but seldom feed in water. They are expert divers when pressed by danger or predators.

All geese have loud, trumpeting voices, varying according to species, deeper in the larger forms, lighter in the small ones. Most geese establish their nests in vegetation near water, sometimes on ledges or cliffs and rocks. Aquatic plants, reeds, rushes and grasses are cut by the bill and used as materials for constructing the nest. Five to ten eggs, white or cream in colour, form a normal clutch.

Geese are easily accustomed to captivity and soon become tame, even when captured as adults. Birds normally breed and nest in their third year although some may be five years of age before pairing takes place. The different species live well in mixed flocks, but pens of individual species are more successful for propagation and more easily managed. All geese are hardy and easy to feed.

Their preferred food is grass, so pens and aviaries should be planted with barley, wheat, rye or oat grass. Many species will not nest unless fresh green grass is available, especially during their breeding season. Lettuce, celery, hydroponic grass, alfalfa, grass clippings and other green food may be eaten. Wheat, barley, milo, oats and corn grains are eaten readily. Young geese or goslings may be hatched under domestic hens or by artificial incubation. Goslings feed well on hydroponic grasses, comfrey, kale and other greens, which should be shredded or cut finely. Soaked biscuit, pelleted game chow and egg food may be added to advantage.

Diet for Geese (Each Feeding)

247g wheat, milo or barley.
57g bread.
247g hydroponic grass or lettuce or celery trimmings.
170 g comfrey.

113 g Purina F & M Chow.
Oyster shell (hen-size) free choice.

Note: Geese are fed twice daily at 7.00 am and 4.30 pm.

Ducks

The smallest members of the waterfowl group are the ducks. They live on lakes, ponds and rivers in all parts of the world. Ducks have webbed feet and are expert swimmers. They are also powerful fliers and some species have been clocked at 60 miles per hour (96 kph). Most are migratory birds. They fly in perfect formation, usually in 'V' shaped lines, for hundreds of miles.

Wild ducks live on grain, acorns, snails, water plants, fish and small insects. Some dive under the surface of the water for food and often go all the way to the bottom of the pond, river or bay to feed on clams and other favourite morsels. Ducks' feathers are covered with a natural oil from an oil gland at the base of the tail. This makes the feathers waterproof and prevents soaking of the downy undercoat that keeps the bird warm.

Among the most familiar groups of ducks are: perching ducks, thirteen species; shelducks, seven species; dabbling or surface-feeding ducks, thirty-nine; pochards, fifteen; stiff-tailed ducks, nine; sea ducks, thirty; and the whistling ducks, which are sometimes called the 'tree swans', nine.

The Wood Duck (*Aix sponsa*) and the Mandarin Duck (*Aix galericulata*) are two of the better known perching ducks. They have long legs and sharp toenails which enable them to climb, perch and nest in tree holes. The shelducks are the most goose-like of the ducks, and perhaps the most colourful. They have only seasonal migration and are Old World ducks. They usually live in small flocks and often feed on paddocks well away from water as well as on tidal flats and estuaries. All have bond patterns. When on grass, their diet should be supplemented with mixed grain, rich pelleted food and additional green food.

The Pintail or Sprig (*Anas acuta*), greyhound of the waterfowl family, is an excellent representative of the dabbling ducks, as is the well-known Mallard (*Anas platyrhynchos*), ancestor of our domestic ducks. Pochards are fresh-water diving ducks with large feet and strongly-lobed hind toes. The legs are widely spread, short and placed farther back on the body than the dabbling ducks. The Canvasback (*Aythya valisineria*) is a

Daily Diets for Ducks

Species	Grain (g)	Green Food (g)	Purina F & M Chow (g)	Pellets (g)
Perching Duck:				
Wood Duck (*Aix sponsa*)	Millet: 247	Duck weed: 28 Hydroponic grass: 28	28	Trout Chow: 28
Shelduck:				
Moluccan (Black-backed) Shelduck (*Tadorna radjah*)	Wheat: 247 Milo: 247	Duck weed: 57 Hydroponic grass: 57	57	Trout Chow: 28 Dog food: 28
Pochards:				
Rosy-billed Pochard (*Netta peposaca*)	Wheat: 247 Milo: 247	Duck weed: 57 Hydroponic grass: 57	57	Dog food: 28
Dabbling duck:				
Mallard (*Anas platyrhynchos*)	Red Wheat: 247 or Milo: 247 or Corn: 247	Duck weed: 57 Hydroponic grass: 57 Lettuce or grass cuttings may also be fed.	57	Dog food: 28
Stiff-tailed duck:				
North American Ruddy Duck (*Oxyura jamaicensis*)	Millet: 28	Duck weed: 247	Bread 28	Trout Chow: 28
Whistling Duck:				
White-faced (*Dendrocygna viduata*)	Cracked corn or Milo: 247	Hydroponic grass: 57 Comfrey: 28	57	Dog food: 28

Fresh water and free choice oyster shell or grit are necessary at all times.

member of this group. The stiff-tailed ducks are characterized by several unusual features in addition to the long, stiffened tail feathers that serve as underwater rudders. The large feet are placed so far back on the body that it is difficult for these birds to walk on land. Adapted for diving, the wings are so short that flight is made difficult. The Ruddy ducks, found in both the Americas, are a well-known member of this group.

The sea ducks, which include Eiders, Scoters and Mergansers, are superb diving birds with specialized feeding habits. No diet is included for this group as it is extremely specialized and is rarely kept successfully in captivity. Whistling ducks have been placed in the genus *Dendrocygna*. The long necks, long legs and large feet combine to produce a distinctive appearance.

The great majority of species of ducks have been kept and are being bred in captivity. Their food, consisting of seeds and water weeds, is easily supplied. Being sociable, they live well in mixed groups on extensive grounds with large ponds. In smaller enclosures and pools it is safer to keep one pair of each species as excess males will interfere with successful breeding.

Many ducks are raised in small pens when an unlimited quantity of suitable food, particularly duck weed, with all of the insect and mollusc life it contains, can be supplied. Pens which are 1.8×3.6 m in size, half land and half water, boarded all around to insure privacy to one pair of birds, have proven practical for several breeders.

In areas where predators are abundant, such as owls, hawks, cats and weasels, it is necessary to keep ducks in pens covered with wire netting.

Because of the diversity in diets of several groups of ducks, one representative diet for each group is listed.

Screamers

The three species of screamers, the Horned (*Anhima cornuta*), Black-necked (*Chauna chavaria*) and Crested (*Chauna torquata*) are aquatic birds of the wet marshes or warm and tropical areas of South America. They have all been raised by the authors. All are mainly vegetarian.

They are about the size of large geese, 70 to 90 cm in length. Their legs are longer than those of geese, with large feet which are partially webbed. The legs are thick and strong and the toes are remarkably long. Their wings are large and broad, each armed with two powerful spurs used chiefly for defence. Good swimmers, they have a layer of air sacs beneath the skin which provides a living air mattress for them. The name 'screamer' refers to their loud, strident cries.

Outside the breeding season, when the birds form pairs, screamers live in troops of twenty-five to one hundred birds. They fly and soar well, calling in raucous voices that can be heard a mile away. When disturbed, they fly to the nearest grove of low trees or shrubs to perch and rest.

The Horned Screamer inhabits the flood forests of the Amazon delta. It is black with white on the crown, neck and under-parts. The 'horn' on its forehead may be 15 cm in length. The Crested Screamer, a grey bird with narrow black and white rings around the neck, has a short crest. It lives in the pampas regions of the LaPlata states, often in the company

[37]

of cattle. The Black-necked Screamer is also crested and has a wide black neck band. It is found along the forest rivers of Colombia and Venezuela.

These birds build a shallow nest of rushes and reeds on the ground, usually in grassy marshes. Two to six chalky-white eggs form a normal clutch, which takes forty-two to forty-four days to hatch. Both sexes incubate the eggs. The chicks are covered with yellow down and follow the parents around like little goslings a few hours after hatching.

All live well in captivity. They may be kept safely with chickens or waterfowl in farm yards. They become very tame and affectionate, making excellent pets.

Diet for Screamers (Each Feeding)

170 g duck weed (*Lemna minor*).
170 g water cress (*Nasturtium officinale*).
170 g hydroponic grass (barley, oats, or wheat).
170 g lettuce (least desirable).
28 g Purina Trout Chow (40% protein).
28 g cubed wheat bread with ¼ tsp (1 g) Wheat Germ Oil on bread.
28 g ground meal.
113 g cracked corn or milo.
Oyster shell (hen-size): free choice.

Note: Fed twice daily; grain fed only in the morning.

Falconiformes

VULTURES · SECRETARY BIRD · OSPREY · EAGLES ·
FALCONS · HAWKS · KITES · CARACARAS

About 280 species of birds belong to the Falconiformes, or day-flying birds of prey. In most, the bill is strong and sharply hooked, with a fleshy cere across the top through which the nostrils open. The legs and feet are strong. The claws or talons are sharp and piercing, adapted for holding large and small prey. The wings are large, some rounded, others pointed. The plumage is variable with sexes usually being similar. Females are larger than males in most forms.

All of this order will eat meat, fish or insects. The larger kinds can be fed meat in large pieces or on large bones. The smaller kinds thrive best on whole small animals such as rabbits, pigeons, rats, mice, sparrows, grubs and insects. The larger ones should have such food twice weekly, in order to obtain the fur, feathers and internal organs which appear to be essential for their good health. Vultures will live well on fresh meat and there is no reason to feed carrion or spoiled meat. Ospreys feed almost exclusively on fish.

The disappearance of several birds of prey has stimulated research in various parts of the world in artificial breeding of the birds. Laboratories have been developing good nutritional diets for captive birds of prey. It is essential that more breeding programmes for endangered and threatened birds of prey are set up. Fortunately, many species have great potential for recovery and the enlargement of their present remnant populations.

New World Vultures

There are seven species of New World Vultures still in existence. This group (*Vulturidae*) is found in both temperate and tropical Americas—in forests, grasslands, brushlands, deserts and mountains. They vary in size from 64 to 132 cm in length. They feed on fresh or decomposing animal corpses. Most also catch living mammals and birds. Eggs from sea bird rookeries are the favourite food of the Andean Condor which is the largest of this group. None build nests. They simply lay their eggs on the ground, in tree cavities or on ledges along cliffs above the sea.

The eggs of the birds of prey are rounded at one end and pointed at the other. This shape prevents them from rolling out of a stick nest or off a rocky ledge. One to three eggs are usually laid. The eggs may be greenish, white or buff with or without markings of grey or reddish-brown. Incubation periods vary from thirty-nine to forty-one days in the smaller vultures to fifty-four to fifty-six days for the largest members, the condors.

The chicks are naked when hatched, but soon are covered with white, grey or buff down. They are completely dependent on the parent birds and are fed by regurgitation by both parents until able to leave the nest, feed themselves and fly. Four of the seven forms have propagated in captivity: Andean Condor (*Vultur gryphus*); King Vulture (*Sarcorhamphus papa*); Black Vulture (*Coragyps atratus*); and Turkey Vulture (*Cathartes aura*).

Old World Vultures

There are fourteen species of Old World Vultures (Aegypiinae) and most are carrion eaters. The Cinerous or Hooded Vulture (*Neophron monachus*) is the largest bird of prey in the Old World with a wingspread of 280 cm. Black in colour, it has a 'monk's collar' which protects both the front and rear of the neck. It feeds on dead animals and human refuse. Its range is from southern Europe to China and it prefers wooded areas.

The Griffon Vulture (*Gyps fulvus*) has dark buff body plumage with the head and neck covered by white down. It has a long, white ruff. It is found from Spain to northern India.

The Pondicherry or Indian Black Vulture (*Sarcogyps calvus*) is indigenous to India, Burma and the Malay Peninsula. Picturesque, it is black with huge reddish lappets of skin hanging from its face. It has patches of white on its chest and above the thighs. It nests in trees and lays one egg.

The White-headed Vulture (*Trigonoceps occipitalis*) is a resident of India, Burma and Indo-China. Slate-grey in body colour, the white patch on its back is conspicuous when taking a 'sun bath'. There is a white collar around the base of the neck.

The Lammergeyer or Bearded Vulture (*Gypaetus barbatus*) is found in remote mountain areas of southern Europe, Africa and Asia. Powerful and strong, it has been seen to knock an animal off a cliff, then descend to devour the injured prey. This vulture also drops bones from great heights to shatter them, then lands to eat the bone fragments. The Lammergeyer must be considered the most endangered of these birds, as in recent years it has fallen victim of poison baits and control measures which were directed primarily at jackals and vermin.

The Egyptian Vulture (*Neophron percnopterus*) ranges throughout Africa, southern Europe and south-western Asia. It is the smallest of the vultures, 53 to 69 cm in length and weighing 1.85 kg. Its body plumage is white with some black on the wings. The face is bare, the rest of its head and neck completely feathered. A true scavenger of carcasses of dead animals, this bird too has suffered from indiscriminate poison campaigns and is no longer as common as it once was.

If vultures and condors are to be bred successfully in captivity, they must be fed very carefully balanced diets. Pieces of horse meat and chicken necks may keep them alive, but reproduction will not occur.

Daily Diets for New and Old World Vultures

Mixture No. 1
ZuPreem Bird of Prey Diet: 454 g.
Supplement with choice of: 1 New World Opossum (454 g) or 2 Norway rats (800 g); 1 guinea pig (850 g); 2 domestic chicks (51 g); 2 Northern Anchovy (40 g).

Mixture No. 2
227 g Purina Game Bird Breeder Layena.
227 g ground meat.
Supplemented with choice of: 1 New World Opossum (454 g) or 2 Norway rats (800 g); 1 guinea pig (850 g); 2 domestic chicks (51 g); 2 Northern Anchovy (40 g).

Formulation of diets is influenced by the available foodstuff.

Daily Diet for Hand-feeding Vulturine Nestlings

38 g minced horse meat (sprinkled with 9 g meat tenderizer three hours before feeding and kept in refrigerator at 37.8 °C–100 °F).
Egg (yolk only): 5 g.
Mice, internal organs, also sprinkled with tenderizer: 5 g. Two drops multiple vitamin, ABDEC, Avitron.

The pepsins in the meat tenderizer break down the enzymes in the meat to aid in digestion by the chicks. The amount of food should be adjusted to body condition. This mixture will supply the vitamins and minerals needed for maintenance and reproduction of birds of prey.

Secretary Bird

The Secretary Bird (*Sagittarius serpentarius*) lives in the African savannah country south of the Sahara desert. The crest of long plumes, suggesting a group of quill pens stuck behind the ear of old-time secretaries, is responsible for the name. Long-legged, their height may reach 1 m and the wingspread 2 m. Unlike other hawks or vultures, this bird hunts on foot and kills its prey by stunning it with powerful blows of the feet. Famed as a snake killer, it prefers pythons and vipers as prey. Small mammals, large insects (especially locusts), young birds and lizards are also eaten daily.

In captivity, ground horse meat, supplemented with common snakes, mice, rats, domestic chicks, lizards and fresh eggs may be fed. Considered beneficial because of its snake-killing ability, the secretary bird is protected by game laws wherever it exists. It is unlikely that the layman will ever import this bird for private collections and fewer zoological gardens are now exhibiting it.

Osprey

The Fish Hawk or Osprey (*Pandion haliaetus*) is never found far from water. It ranges along most coasts, larger lakes and rivers of the continental land masses of the world. It has also colonized on oceanic islands where no other hawks have been able to survive. This beautiful raptor is 60 to 66 cm in length, with a wingspread of 48 to 54 cm. The body plumage is brown above, white below. The white crown, black eye patch and wrist patch on the under wing, narrow black band on the tail are good field marks.

The feet are large with four toes of equal length instead of unequal as in all other raptors. The outer toe is reversible as in the owls, so that it can grasp its prey with two toes in front and two behind. Each toe is tipped with a long down-curved nail, and the toes have rough, stiff projections on the underside to help hold slippery prey. The osprey lives entirely on fish which it catches alive. An expert fisherman, with keen eyesight, this bird hovers above water at heights of 500 m or more and dives with feet extended, wings half closed.

It splashes to the surface in a few seconds with a fish grasped tightly in both talons. The fish is carried to a convenient tree, high rock or to the nest to be eaten. Prey may weigh as much as 2 kg, but usually smaller fish, 100 to 200 g, are captured. The daily food requirement is about 400 g of fish. The fish it eats are mainly species of little economic importance.

Nests are made of sticks, usually in trees. Two to three eggs are laid. The eggs, beautifully coloured, are white or rust, blotched with deep brown. Incubation lasts thirty-five days, and it is eight to ten weeks before the chicks are fledged.

Ospreys should not be kept as pets or under captive conditions. They will live only a short time, even with the best of care. Once plentiful in this country and Europe, the osprey is threatened with extinction due to industrialization and urbanization.

The following diet for osprey is given only so that injured birds or orphaned fledglings which may have been rescued can be fed and, it is hoped, released back into their natural habitat.

The daily requirement for osprey in captivity is 400 g of one of the following: Pacific Mackerel (*Pneumatophorus diego*); Mullet (*Mugil cephalus*); Pacific Herring (*Clupea pallasii*); Sardine (*Sandinops caerulea*); Surf Smelt (*Hypomesus pretiosus*); Bay Smelt (*Atherinops affinis*) or Queenfish (*Seriphus politus*).

The first osprey sanctuary in the United States was established at Crane Prairie Reservoir in the Deschutes National Forest of central Oregon in 1970. More than 4050 hectares (10,000 acres) have been set aside there for the protection of the osprey and the survival needs are being studied by the US Forest Service, the Department of Agriculture and the Oregon State Game Commission.

Eagles, Falcons, Hawks, Kites (Accipitridae)

The ability of birds to hunt living prey is most highly developed in this group. They are distinguished by lethal features which they possess to overcome their prey. They hunt by day, soaring and circling high in the air in search of food. Some patrol fields and marshes. Other birds take birds in the air, diving at speeds of 200 miles per hour (320 kph). Their bodies are strong and compact, the head is usually rounded. The large

Daily Diets for Eagles

Species	Fish (g)	ZuPreem (g)	Rodents (g)	Mammals/ Poultry (g)	Natural Food
Bald Eagle (*Haliaeetus leucocephalus*)	907-mackerel, anchovy, smelt	120	400-rats		Salmon, mullet
Golden Eagle (*Aquila chrysaetos*)		120	400-rats	850-guinea pig or 907-rabbit	Rabbit, ground squirrel, marmot
Bateleur Eagle (*Terathopius ecaudatus*)		120	400-rats 20-mouse		Rats, snakes, lizards, shrews, tortoises, bird eggs
Monkey-eating Eagle (*Pithecophaga jefferyi*)		120		454-opossum 850-guinea pig	Green macaque, junglefowl, peacock pheasant
Harpy Eagle (*Harpia harpyia*)		120	400-rats	850-guinea pig 1814-chicken	Sloth, macaws, coatis, agouti, capuchin, wooly, squirrel monkeys
Wedge-tailed Eagle (*Aquila audax*)		120	400-rats	907-rabbit 1814-chicken	Rabbits, dingo pups, rats
Martial Eagle (*Polemaetus bellicosus*)		120	400-rats		Hyrax, baboons, jackal, guinea-fowl
African Fish Eagle (*Haliaeetus vocifer*)	907-mackerel, anchovy, smelt	120			Tilapia, mullet
Steller's Sea Eagle (*Haliaeetus pelagicus*)	907-mackerel anchovy, smelt	120			Bonita, herring, shad, greyling

eyes have highly developed vision. The beak is hooked and shaped for tearing. The cutting edges of the upper mandible project like scissors over those of the lower mandible. The beak is covered by a soft cere at the base of the upper mandible. The foot is strong and short, with long talons to form grasping tools for seizing prey. The flight and tail feathers are large.

Many forest birds of prey possess a crest, which is raised and expanded to show aggression. Among them are great eagles which weigh up to 9 kg and have a wingspread of 180 cm. This contrasts with the small falconets which are 17 cm in length. The plumage of most of this group is brown, black or grey. Females are usually larger than the males. The voices are varied and not musical, consisting of screams, whistles, mews, cackles and yelps.

Most pair for life and nest on stick platforms in trees. Others prefer nests on rock cliffs and some hawks even nest on the ground. Both sexes feed and care for the young. By far the majority of raptors are adapted to capturing prey, which may consist of insects, snails, frogs, toads, fish, snakes, small birds and mammals. A few will eat carrion if natural food is absent.

Falcons

The thirty-five species of falcons are fast-flying birds of prey with large heads, long narrow wings and long tails. These wide-ranging, day-hunting birds exhibit as much variety in habits as they do in size. The Gyrfalcon (*Falco rusticolus*), which is 50 cm in length, lives in the Arctic tundra. It is snow white in colour and is the largest of the true falcons. The smallest may be the tiny Red-legged Falconet (*Microhierax caerulescens*) from south-eastern Asia which is 15 cm in length. In medieval times, the sport of falconry depended on this group of birds.

The Peregrine Falcon (*Falco peregrinus*), also known as the Duck Hawk, has some sixteen geographical races. It inhabits the entire northern hemisphere, Australia, South Africa, Patagonia, and the Falkland Islands. This large falcon, 38 cm in length, is dark in colour with a black moustache. The bird hunts from several hundred feet in the air, swooping down at tremendous speed upon its prey. It dives at speeds which have been clocked at 60 to 90 miles per hour (100–150 kph). Pigeons, ducks, starlings, thrushes, lapwings and larks are hunted. Peregrines are clean killers. They strike their prey once with the feet in passing, usually breaking the prey's back or crippling it so it falls helplessly to the ground. Peregrine falcons do not kill for fun. They kill only to provide food for themselves or their fledglings. (See table on p. 46.)

Hawks, Kites, Caracaras

Hawks, kites and caracaras are recognized as being of great value to agriculture because of the millions of rodents, snakes, grasshoppers and other insects they destroy annually. Some forty species of goshawks in the subfamily Accipitridae belong in this group. These hunting hawks have long legs and rounded wings. They live largely on small birds and mammals.

Daily Diets for Falcons

Species	Poultry (g)	Ducks (g)	Rodents (g)	Insects (g)	Natural Food
Gyrfalcon (Falco rusticolus)	125-coturnix quail 907-chicken	775-pekin duck	850-guinea pig 907-rabbit		Lemming, arctic hare
Peregrine Falcon (Falco peregrinus)	454-pigeon 125-chick 125-coturnix quail	775-pekin duck			Pigeon, starling, duck
Prairie Falcon (Falco mexicanus)	125-chick		400-rat 20-mouse		Cottontail, mice, ground squirrel
Merlin (Pigeon Hawk) (Falco columbarius)	226-dove 125-chick 125-coturnix quail		20-mouse	5-mealworms 5-grasshoppers 5-crickets	Sparrows, linnets, moles, lizards, beetles, crickets, grasshoppers
Red-legged Falconet (Microhierax caerulescens)	6-day-old coturnix quail		2-'pinky' mouse (baby)	16-mealworms 16-crickets 16-beetles	Larks, quail, grasshoppers, crickets, dragonflies.

The true hawks, in the sub-family Buteoninae, are world-wide in distribution. There are some ninety species in the group of broad-winged, soaring hawks. Another seventeen species of slender, long-winged, long-tailed birds have prominent facial discs. They are cosmopolitan in distribution where there is open land. They are placed in the sub-family Circinae.

Seven species of White-tailed Kites of the sub-family Elaninae are light-coloured raptors with graceful flight. They are found in the temperate and tropical areas. Ninety-eight per cent of their food consists of rodents.

Daily Diets for Hawks, Kites and Caracaras

Species	ZuPreem (g)	Rodents (g)	Poultry (g)	Natural Food
Goshawk (*Accipiter gentilis*)	454	400-rat	454-pigeon 125-coturnix quail	Pheasant, wood pigeon, crows, magpies, grouse, hare
Cooper's Hawk (*Accipiter cooperii*)	227	200-ground squirrel 400-rat 20-mouse	125-coturnix quail 51-chick	Pigeons, doves, quail, chicken, ground squirrel
Marsh Hawk (*Circus cyaneus*)	227	400-rat 20-mouse		Frogs, lizards, field mice, rabbits, snakes
Sharp-shinned Hawk (*Accipiter striatus*)	115		125-coturnix quail	Flickers, chickadee, dove, quail, housefinch, bluebird
Red-tailed Hawk (*Buteo jamaicensis*)	454	907-rabbit 400-rat 20-mouse		snakes, jack rabbits, rats, ground squirrel
Harris's Hawk (*Parabuteo unicinctus*)	227	400-rat 20-mouse	51-chick	Wood rats, chipmunks
Red-shouldered Hawk (*Buteo lineatus*)	227	150-ground squirrel 400-rat 20-mouse	51-chick	Mice, birds, snakes, frogs, grasshoppers, centipedes, spiders, snails, crawfish
White-tailed Kite (*Elanus leucurus*)		102-mouse		Field mice, lizards, snakes, grasshoppers
Everglade Kite (*Rostrhamus sociabilis*)			125-coturnix quail	Water snails, water snakes
Audubon's Caracara (*Polyborus cheriway auduboni*)	454	400-rat 20-mouse	51-chick	Carrion fish, snakes, cottontails, insects
Yellow-headed Caracara (*Milvago chimachima*)	227	20-mouse	51-chick	Carrion, eggs, palm nuts, mice, small birds, insects, ticks, lizards

The honey buzzards, with thirteen species in the sub-family Perninae, are long-winged, long-tailed kites. Swallow-tailed and Hook-billed Kites are included in this group. The true kites are placed in the sub-family Milvinae, which consists of fourteen species. The Plumbeous, Mississippi and Snail Kites are the best known of this group.

The carrion hawks or caracaras, nine species in number, live in the New World, mainly in South America. This group, of the sub-family Polyborinae, inhabits open country, seashores and lightly wooded country. Many are scavengers, eating road kills, beached fish, snakes and invertebrates. Their way of life and eating habits are reminiscent of vultures. Although the Audubon's Caracara (*Polyborus cheriway auduboni*) is the national bird of Mexico, it nests in the prairie regions of central Florida around Kissimmee prairies and Lake Okeechobee. The nest is placed in the centre of cabbage palms. Two eggs form a clutch and both sexes incubate the eggs for four or five weeks. The chicks learn to fly in about ten weeks.

Caracaras have strong legs and walk well on the ground. They are seen in company with vultures at a carcass and have been known to drive vultures away from a meal, walk in and eat the choice parts first.

Galliformes

MEGAPODES · CURASSOWS · GUANS · CHACHALACAS · GROUSE · PHEASANTS · PEACOCKS · CHICKENS · GUINEAFOWL · TURKEYS · QUAILS · PARTRIDGES · FRANCOLINS

Megapodes

The megapodes form a small family of twelve species. The members are called maleos, mound builders, scrub fowl, brush turkeys, incubator birds or thermometer birds. In size, they range from 50 to 70 cm in length. Most are plainly coloured in shades of dark brown, black or grey. One species is crested. Others have heads bare, wattled or casqued. The sexes are alike. All are 'big footed' with strong legs, feet and claws. They feed largely on fallen fruit and seeds, but small animals, rodents, gastropods, including marine snails and crabs, may also be eaten.

This family, Megapodidae, is from Australia, New Guinea and the East Indian islands. They are the only birds whose eggs are not incubated by body heat. The heat of the sun, fermentation of vegetable matter or volcanic action is used for incubation. The Maleo Fowl (*Macrocephalon maleo*) uses only the sun's heat. Holes dug along the shore which are in direct sunshine are used. The Australian Scrub Fowl (Common Scrub Hen) (*Megapodius freycinet*) selects places to lay its eggs which are heated by volcanic action.

The Brush Turkey (*Alectura lathami*) of Australia constructs huge brood mounds which are always in deep forests and therefore completely shaded. This bird depends entirely on the heat of fermentation of the vegetation for incubation. The male scratches leaves, debris and plant fragments with his large feet to make the brood mound. This may measure 3 metres in diameter and 1.5 metres in height. Ten to thirteen eggs, white or buff in colour, are laid by the hen and placed in holes in the mound. The male bird controls the temperature of this natural incubator by opening and closing the mound. In New Guinea, the natives protect the nesting sites and harvest the eggs for eating.

Incubation periods range from fifty-six to sixty-three days. The chicks dig out of the mounds when hatched and are completely on their own.

They never know their parents as neither cares for them after they are out of the mound.

Daily Diet for Megapodes

Purina F & M Chow: 14 g.
Bread: 11 g whole wheat.
Peanuts: 2, in shell.
Egg: ½ hard-boiled, crumbled.
Berries or greens: 5 g, choice of eugenia, pyracantha, cotoneaster, mulberry, sow thistle, dock, swiss chard, New Zealand spinach, comfrey, hydroponic sprouted (7-day) oats or barley.
Insects: 5 g mealworms, beetles or 1 garden snail.
Grain: 5 g cracked corn, milo or wheat.
Oyster shell: free choice (hen-size).

Curassows, Guans and Chachalacas

The thirty-eight species of curassows, guans and chachalacas are little known to many aviculturists and game breeders. Their care and feeding is undemanding. The curassows are the largest, 100 cm in length. Guans are second, 75 cm in length, and the chachalacas are the size of most pheasants, 62 cm. They are distributed from southern Texas and into Mexico as far south as Paraguay and into northern Argentina. All are found in subtropical or tropical Americas.

These three groups are adapted to living in trees. They walk about lightly on thin branches in the tops of trees, feeding on fruits, blossoms, shoots, leaves, reeds, lizards and insects which abound in tropical forests. Occasionally they are seen feeding on the forest floor, but when disturbed they fly into the trees. Calls are loud and harsh.

They are heavy bodied with broad wings. Their tails are medium long. The legs and feet are large and strong. Generally they are black or reddish-brown in colour, often with white markings. Some are crested and a few are helmeted. Fleshy wattles are found on the throats of some species, while others have red, yellow and blue knobs at the base of the bill.

Most of the family build platform nests in trees, vines or in bushes in the forests or thickets. Twigs, climbing plant stems, leaves, grass and palm fronds are carried to the nesting site while still fresh and green.

Two to five eggs form a clutch. The eggs are large and granulated. Only the female incubates the eggs while the male guards the nest. Incubation periods range from thirty to thirty-two days for the curassows, twenty-eight days for the guans and twenty-four days for the chachalacas.

The eggs will hatch well under domestic hens and the chicks are easy to raise. If chicks are raised alone, a low perch should be placed in the brooder for them to roost on. The brooder must be covered as the chicks are able to fly and perch in forty-eight hours after hatching. They will eat berries and greens hung from the top of the brooder in bunches within reach of the species.

Daily Diet for Curassows, Guans, Chachalacas

Grain: 5 g maize, milo or hulled oats.
Fruits and berries: 40 g, choice of plums, dates, figs, cherries, tomato, avocado, papaya, grapes, mulberry, raspberry, blackberry, elderberry, eugenia, pyracantha.
Greens: 5 g, choice of sow thistle, New Zealand spinach, swiss chard, comfrey, 7-day hydroponic sprouted oats.
Trout Chow: 5 g.
Egg: $\frac{1}{2}$ hard-boiled.
Bread: 11 g.
Nuts: 7 g.
Insects: 5 g mealworms, beetles or crickets.
Oyster shell: 5 g, hen-size.

Daily Diet for Curassow, Guan, Chachalaca chicks

*Baked custard: 2 g.
Blueberries: 1 g.
Insects: 1 g mealworms or crickets.
Greens: 1 g finely shredded lettuce when birds are 7 days old and after.
Minerals: 3 g Vionate multivitamin powder mixed with custard.

---

* Baked custard: 0.6 litre hot milk, 4 tablespoons sugar, 2 eggs, pinch salt. Beat eggs slightly, add salt and sugar and stir until sugar is dissolved. Add milk gradually to this mixture. Pour into buttered cups or pudding dish, placed in pan of hot water. Bake at 160° to 180°C (325° to 350°F) until firm in centre (test with knife blade which will come out clean when custard is done).

Grouse

The eighteen species of grouse in the family Tetraonidae are easily distinguished from other fowl-like birds due to their having feathered legs. In some, the toes are also feathered. They have a short bill which curves down and the nostrils are covered with feathers. Often there is a patch of brightly coloured skin over the eye. All have the hind toe shorter than the front three and elevated. The short necks are adorned with inflatable bare spots or tufts of erectile feathers. Most are polygamous with elaborate courtship displays.

There is a broad range in size. The White-tailed Ptarmigan (*Lagopus leucurus*) from the circumpolar regions is 25 cm in length. The giant Capercaillie (*Tetrao urogallus*) is 85 cm in length. Its home is the forests of Eurasia and Siberia. Plumage is coloured in browns, greys and black. Three Ptarmigans turn white in winter. The sexes are alike in several species with the cock being much larger than the hen.

Grouse are usually browsers and grazers. They feed on buds, berries, twiglets, leaves and fruit. They also eat seeds, conifer needles and snails. In summer they also eat insects.

Unfortunately, grouse are susceptible to many infections of the crop when in captivity and are difficult to keep. Earthworms and snails are the hosts of several stomach and intestinal worms and should not be fed unless they are disease-free.

All of the grouse family nest on the ground in simple depressions in the grass or soil. The female makes the nest, incubates the eggs and rears the chicks. Six to sixteen eggs may be laid, usually one clutch each year. Incubation periods range from twenty-one to twenty-eight days. The chicks are able to run about and forage for food a few hours after hatching. They are closely guarded by the hens.

The Ruffed Grouse (*Bonasa umbellus*) which ranges from Alaska to Canada and into the USA as far as the mountains of Georgia is the most common grouse seen in captivity. Game breeders raise most of them in pens with raised wire floors so that parasites will not be picked up from the soil. Sharp-tailed Grouse, Ptarmigan, Capercaillie, Black Grouse, Blue Grouse, Spruce Grouse and Ruffed Grouse are some of the species presently being kept in captivity successfully.

Daily Diet for Grouse and Partridge

Fruits: 14 g, choice of apples, cherries, plums, grapes, strawberries, blackberries, raspberries, gooseberries, cranberries, blueberries, cotoneaster.

Greens: 28 g, choice of chickweed, dandelion, pine needles, willow, birch buds, rose-hips.

Insects: 14 g, choice of crickets, mealworms, grubs, beetles, moths, caterpillars, grasshoppers, cutworms.

Egg: ½ hard–boiled, crumbled.

Trout Chow: 14 g.

Minerals: 5 g Vionate multivitamin supplement, sprinkled on greens.

Nuts: 28 g, choice of beechnuts, hazelnuts, acorns, chestnuts, pine nuts.

Pheasants

The family Phasianidae, pheasants, is the largest and most varied group of gallinaceous birds. There are 177 species, including partridges, franco-lins, peafowl, junglefowl and quail. They range in size from the tiny Chinese Painted Quail (*Excalfactoria chinensis*) which is 15 cm in length to the giant Indian Blue Peafowl|(*Pavo cristatus*) which is 230 cm in length.

The pheasants include some of the most beautiful birds in the avian world. Their brilliant colours rival those of hummingbirds and birds of paradise. The natural home of pheasants is Asia, Africa, Malaysia and the neighbouring islands and Asia Minor. All are Old World birds. They have been introduced into many countries for hunting. The Ring-necked Pheasant (*Phasianus colchicus*) from China is so familiar to laymen in North America that many believe them to be native birds.

Certain characteristics identify all of the pheasants. The nostrils are unfeathered, there is no inflatable airsac on the neck, the feet are naked and clean, with few exceptions, and many have heavy spurs on the legs above the hind toe. The bill is small and hen-like. Some tails are very short, others extremely long. Many pheasants are crested and wattled. The sexes are usually alike.

Females construct simple nests protected by long grass, bushes or tree roots. Eggs number from two in the Peacock and Argus Pheasants to six to twelve in the Ring-necked Pheasants. The female incubates the eggs and rears the chicks alone. In general, cocks mate with several hens during the breeding season. Most have loud and harsh voices.

All of the pheasants, with very few exceptions, live and breed well in captivity. A number have adapted themselves to new climates and are established in American and Eurasian aviaries. Others are still uncommon because they have not been imported from remote areas and habitats. A number of pheasants are in danger as their habitats are gradually being invaded by humans and are being destroyed.

Daily Diet for: Chinese Ring-necked (*Phasianus colchicus lorquatus*); Golden (*Chrysolophus pictus*); Lady Amherst's (*Chrysolophus amherstiae*); Silver (*Lophura nycthemera*); Swinhoe's (*Lophura swinhoei*); Siamese Fireback (*Lophura diardi*); White-crested Kalij (*Lophura leucomelana*); Elliot's (*Syrmaticus ellioti*); Mikado (*Syrmaticus mikado*); Ijima's Copper (*Syrmaticus soemmerrengii ijimae*); and Reeve's (*Syrmaticus reevesii*) Pheasants

Purina F & M Chow: 14 g.
Trout Chow: 5 g, mixed with F & M Chow.
Choice of greens: 43 g spinach, dock, sow thistle, swiss chard, comfrey, 7-day hydroponic oats, barley or wheat sprouts.
Fruits or berries: 14 g apple ($\frac{1}{4}$), eugenia, pyracantha, cotoneaster, mulberry, blackberries, gooseberries.
Choice of grain: 14 g milo, wheat, soybean or corn, fed in evening.
Egg: $\frac{1}{2}$ hard-boiled, crumbled on Chow.
Oyster shell: 5 g, hen-size (1 tsp).

Daily Diet for Himalayan Monal (*Lophophorus impeyanus*)

Purina F & M Chow: 14 g.
Trout Chow: 5 g, mixed with F & M Chow.
Choice of greens: 43 g spinach, dock, sow thistle, swiss chard, comfrey, 7-day hydroponic oats, barley or wheat sprouts, wild endive roots, dandelions, diced carrots.
Fruits or berries: 14 g apple ($\frac{1}{4}$), eugenia, pyracantha, cotoneaster, mulberry, blackberries, gooseberries.
Choice of grain: 14 g milo, wheat, soybean or corn, maize, buckwheat, fed in evening.
Egg: $\frac{1}{2}$ hard-boiled, crumbled on Chow.
Oyster shell: 5 g, hen-size (1 tsp).

Daily Diet for Satyr Tragopan (*Tragopan satyra*) **and Temminck's Tragopan** (*Tragopan temminckii*)

Purina F & M Chow: 14 g (1 tablespoon).
Trout Chow: 5 g, mixed with F & M Chow (1 teaspoon).
Vegetables: 28 g endive roots, diced carrots or cabbage.
Fruits or berries: 14 g diced apple ($\frac{1}{4}$), cherries, currants, plums, tomatoes, blackberries, raspberries, strawberries, gooseberries, eugenia, pyracantha, or cotoneaster.
Choice of greens: 43 g spinach, dock, sow thistle, comfrey, New Zealand spinach, swiss chard, dandelions, 7-day hydroponic grass, oats or barley.
Egg: 28 g— $\frac{1}{2}$ hard-boiled, crumbled on Chow.
Minerals: 5 g Vionate multivitamin sprinkled on green food.

Daily Diet for: Blue-eared Pheasant (*Crossoptilon auritum*);
Brown-eared Pheasant (*Crossoptilon mantchuricum*) **and White-eared Pheasant** (*Crossoptilon crossoptilon*)

Purina F & M Chow: 14 g.
Trout Chow: 5 g, mixed with F & M Chow.
Vegetables: 28 g endive roots, diced carrots or cabbage.
Fruits or berries: 14 g diced apple ($\frac{1}{4}$), cherries, currants, plums, tomatoes, blackberries, raspberries, strawberries, gooseberries, eugenia, pyracantha or cotoneaster.
Choice of greens: 43 g spinach, dock, sow thistle, comfrey, New Zealand spinach, swiss chard, dandelions, 7-day hydroponic grass, oats or barley.
Egg: 28 g— $\frac{1}{2}$ hard-boiled, crumbled on Chow.
Seeds: paddy rice, hemp.
Minerals: 5 g Vionate multivitamin sprinkled on green food.

Daily Diet for Malayan Great Argus Pheasant (*Argusianus argus*)

Purina F & M Chow: 14 g.
Insects: 5 g mealworms or crickets.
Fruits or berries: 5 g blueberry, mulberry, eugenia *or* canned fruit cocktail or chopped fruit.
Greens: 43 g chickweed, dandelion or watercress.
Egg: 14 g— $\frac{1}{4}$ hard-boiled, crumbled.
Seed: canary or millet seed.

Daily Diet for Germain's Peacock Pheasant (*Polyplectron germaini*) and Palawan Peacock Pheasant (*Polyplectron emphanum*)

Purina F & M Chow: 14 g.
Insects: 5 g mealworms or crickets.
Berries: pyracantha, cotoneaster or eugenia.
Greens: 43 g lantana blossoms, chickweed or dandelion.
Egg: 14 g ($\frac{1}{4}$) hard-boiled egg, crumbled.
Seeds: canary or millet.

Daily Diets for Pheasant Chicks

Tragopans
5 g Game Bird Starter Crumbles.
5 g (1 tsp) shredded lettuce, after two weeks old.
5 g egg custard, for first two weeks.
2 g ($\frac{1}{2}$ tsp) hard-boiled egg, fed after two weeks.
2 blueberries, after two weeks old.
2–4 mealworms or crickets.
5 g Vionate multivitamin supplement sprinkled on egg custard.
5 g bread and milk, fed after fourteen days.

Golden Pheasant, Lady Amherst's, Blue-Eared, Brown-Eared, Mikado, Reeve's chicks
5 g Game Bird Starter Crumbles.
5 g shredded lettuce.
5 g egg custard, for first two weeks.
5 g hard-boiled egg, crumbled on Starter Crumbles.
5 g bread and milk, after fourteen days.
5 g Vionate, sprinkled on green food.

Malay Argus Chicks
5 g Game Bird Starter Crumbles.
2 g ($\frac{1}{2}$ tsp) finely shredded lettuce.
5 g egg custard, for first two weeks.
1–2 mealworms.
2 g hard-boiled egg yolk, crumbled and sprinkled on Crumbles.
5 g bread and milk after fourteen days.
5 g Vionate, sprinkled on green food.

Peacock Pheasant Chicks
5 g Game Bird Starter Crumbles.
2 g finely shredded lettuce.

5 g egg custard, for first two weeks.

1–2 mealworms.

2 g hard-boiled egg yolk, crumbled on Crumbles or mixed with bread.

5 g bread and milk, after fourteen days.

5 g Vionate, sprinkled on greens.

Himalayan Monal Pheasant chicks have the same diet as the Peacock Pheasant chick with the addition of two blueberries, daily. The mealworms are fed twice daily.

Peacocks

The peafowl belong to the same family, Phasianidae, as the pheasants, and are probably the best known of their family. There are two species of peafowl. The Indian Blue Peafowl (*Pavo cristatus*) is found throughout India and Sri Lanka, and is 230 cm in length. The Javanese Green Peafowl (*Pavo muticus*) is 300 cm in length and is from Java and the Malay Peninsula. Both are crested, the Blue with a fan crest and the Green with a straight crest.

Wild peafowl inhabit open, dry forest country and travel in small flocks, feeding on the ground. They fly strongly and roost in trees at night. Berries, fruits, grains, sprouting buds and insects are their chief items of diet. Chopped fresh vegetables and abundant green food must be provided when grass is not accessible to these birds.

In pens, peahens will nest on the ground. Four to eight creamy-buff eggs form a normal clutch. The incubation period is twenty-eight days. The peahen incubates the eggs, broods and rears the peachicks alone. Peachicks are hardy and easy to raise in captivity. Eggs may be hatched in incubators, under broody turkeys or domestic hens.

Daily Diet for Adult Peafowl

Grain: 5 g cracked corn, wheat, milo or buckwheat.

Greens: 9 g sow thistle, New Zealand spinach, swiss chard, dock, dandelions, comfrey, lettuce, hydroponics (7-day) oats or barley.

Vegetables: 14 g diced carrots, squash, asparagus, okra, green beans or peas.

Fruits: 38 g diced apple ($\frac{1}{4}$), tomato, figs, grapes, guavas, eugenia, pyracantha, blackberries, raspberries, gooseberries, avocado or watermelon.

Egg: $\frac{1}{2}$ hard-boiled, crumbled.

Bread: $\frac{1}{2}$ slice.
Purina F & M Chow: 14 g.
Oyster shell: 5 g, hen-size.

Diet for Peachicks (Twice Daily)

5 g Game Bird Starter Crumbles.
2 g egg, $\frac{1}{4}$, hard-boiled, grated.
2 g finely chopped lettuce (remove mid-rib).
5 g Vionate multivitamin supplement, sprinkled on lettuce.

Chickens

Of all wild birds, the fowl, or the one we know as the chicken, has proved to be the easiest to domesticate and the most useful to man. What man has accomplished within recent years of breeding from selected variants has been the development of over 200 breeds and varieties of domestic fowl. Many bear little resemblance to their wild ancestors.

Few people are aware that chickens are pheasants and belong to the family Phasianidae. Junglefowl differ from other pheasants in having both combs and wattles encircling the head and a tail more arched and curved. The four species of junglefowl were the ancestors of all domestic chickens. The Red Junglefowl (*Gallus gallus*), with five well-defined subspecies, ranges from northwestern India through Assam, Burma, Sumatra and Java. The Grey Junglefowl (*Gallus sonneratii*) is found in the hilly and low country of southern and western India. The Ceylon Junglefowl (*Gallus lafayetti*) lives in the damp forests of the mountains as well as the coastal areas in the dry scrub of Sri Lanka. The Green Junglefowl (*Gallus varius*) lives along the seashore and in low-lying valleys of Java and the neighbouring islands.

As an inherent part of our culture, the history of our domesticated fowl is fascinating. Domestication of the junglefowl in China dates back to about 1400 B.C. Domesticated fowl were known around 2500 B.C. in the Indus Valley and a few years later in Iran. They were in Phoenicia and Crete in 1500 B.C., in Mesopotamia around 700 B.C. and came to Greece a few years later. From Greece, domesticated fowl were carried by ship to Rome. Junglefowl appeared in Eurasia very early (around 1500 B.C.). Asiatic fishermen carried them to the Philippines and to many islands in the South Pacific. Junglefowl were brought to the western hemisphere from eastern Asia by the South Pacific seamen.

All junglefowl feed chiefly on seeds, grain, shoots and buds as well as insects. They particularly like the eggs and larvae of termites. They lay their eggs on the ground, under bushes or bamboo thickets. Four to ten eggs, buff or tan in colour, form a normal clutch. The incubation period is twenty-one days, the same as in all domesticated chickens. The female incubates the eggs and both sexes feed and care for the chicks.

Guineafowl

Seven species of guineafowl are found in the world. They are found in Africa, the Malagasy Republic, the Comoro Islands and a small part of Arabia. Only one species, the Helmeted Guineafowl (*Numida meleagris*) from the Guinea coast of western Africa, was domesticated in the fifteenth century and introduced around the world. It is the ancestor of our domestic guineafowl.

All are unmistakably similar, with bare heads and necks, smooth rounded bodies, black, grey and blue plumage, which is generously spotted with white. Some have horny casques or helmets. Three forms have crests or plumes, and several have fleshy wattles at the side of the mouth. Their feet and legs are stout, built for fast running and scratching. The short tails droop and are almost completely hidden by the tail coverts.

Habitats are varied ranging from deep equatorial forests to dry plains and brush country. Food consists of white ants, grasshoppers, beetles, seeds, berries, bulbs, snails, frogs and succulent grasses. They nest on the ground in shallow holes and lay ten to twenty-two eggs. The eggs are tan in colour and finely spotted. The female incubates the eggs for twenty-eight days, broods the 'keets' (chicks) and both sexes feed and care for the young.

Most species of guineafowl travel in good-sized flocks. They may walk over 15 to 25 km daily, following migrating insect populations. Essentially ground birds, they can fly swiftly when necessary. Guineafowl are noisy birds with harsh discordant cackling. As all roost in trees at night, they may be located easily because of their continuous chatter.

The Vulturine Guineafowl (*Acryllium vulturinum*), 60 cm in length, is spectacular and the handsomest of the guineafowl. A native of eastern tropical Africa, the plumage is cobalt blue with long, pointed hackle feathers in white, black and blue, covering its shoulders and breast. A rich maroon collar also adorns the neck.

Crested Guineafowl are found in half a dozen forms across central

Africa and down to Natal. The Plumed Guineafowl (*Guttera plumifera*) has a brush-like tuft of straight feathers on the crown. It inhabits Cameroon and Gabon in western Africa and is 55 cm in length.

The Black Guineafowl (*Agelastes niger*) is the smallest in the group, only 40 cm in length, and is also found in the vast virgin forests in the Cameroon to the lower Congo and eastward into the Ituri forests. This guinea possesses spurs, showing a closer relationship to the junglefowl than do the other guineafowl.

The White-breasted Guineafowl (*Agelastes meleagrides*) is 45 cm in length and is the rarest of the family. It is seldom imported. The head is red and bare. The back is black and the breast is white. The rest of the body is black with a white marbling pattern. Its home is in Ghana and Liberia.

The Pearl and White African varieties of the common Helmeted Guineafowl are the best known and most widely distributed. These birds are very satisfactory to raise in moderate or large flocks.

Daily Diet for Guineafowl

Grain: 14 g, choice of milo, millet or wheat.

Greens: 28 g, choice of fresh chopped alfalfa, hydroponic sprouted barley grass (7.5 cm square, 7 days). On ranches or farms, free range to graze.

Trout Chow: 5 g, mixed with grain.

Minerals: 14 g oyster shell, hen-size.

Daily Diet for Guineafowl Chicks

First two weeks
5 g crumbled, hard-boiled egg, baked corn, fine oatmeal, bread crumbs, cottage cheese, fine grit.

Two to six weeks
5 g Game Bird Crumble pellets, shredded lettuce, 2–4 insects (choice of mealworms, crickets) hard-boiled egg, oyster shell (chick-size).

Six weeks to twelve weeks
14 g Game Bird Crumble pellets, millet seed, chopped alfalfa leaves or hydroponic grass, oats, hard-boiled egg crumbled, oyster shell (chick-size).

After twelve weeks
Adult diet.

Turkeys

The turkey shows many similarities to the pheasant, but several characteristics have placed it in a separate family, Meleagrididae. The turkey
is the largest and heaviest of the game birds, weighing up to 18 kg, and
is too well known to need a description. Turkeys are birds of the woodlands, where they feed on acorns, chestnuts, wild cherries, strawberries,
grapes and beechnuts. When near cultivated farms, they raid corn, milo,
wheat and oat fields. They eat the seeds of chickweed, nibble on tender
shoots and grasses, and catch grasshoppers and crickets and spiders and
other small invertebrates as they patrol the countryside. At night they
flock together and roost in trees.

Turkeys are polygamous and mate with several hens during the breeding season. Their courtship is spectacular, with strutting and spreading
of their metallic plumage and gobbling to impress their harems. Nests
are hidden on the ground where the hen lays eight to fifteen brown spotted
eggs, which are incubated for twenty-eight days.

Turkeys are natives of the New World. Two species are usually recognized. The Wild Turkey (*Meleagris gallopavo*) is the ancestor of all
domestic breeds. It was domesticated by the Indians of Mexico early in
the sixteenth century, probably near Oaxaca. Early explorers introduced
this bird into Eurasia as a game bird and then it was brought to the United
States by the early colonists. The Mexican Wild Turkey is still found
on the Mexican plateau.

Less familiar is the Ocellated Turkey (*Agriocharis ocellata*) of Yucatan,
British Honduras and Guatemala. A small turkey, 90 cm in length, it is
beautifully coloured. It is an endangered species and has never been
domesticated.

Its plumage is iridescent green with 'eyes' of rich purple bordered
with copper. The bare skin of the head is blue rather than red, and it
lacks the beardlike chest tuft seen in the Mexican Wild Turkey and the
Eastern Wild Turkey.

The Eastern Wild Turkey (*Meleagris gallopavo sylvestris*) is a race of
the Mexican Wild Turkey, developed by selective breeding. It is the bird
which was suggested by Benjamin Franklin to be adopted as the national
symbol of the USA rather than the Bald Eagle. The tip of its tail, as well
as the upper tail coverts, are chestnut in colour. Today, it is found in the
wilder parts of Pennsylvania, West Virginia, Kentucky, Missouri and
south in the Ozark Mountains. There are other races in Florida, New
Mexico, Arizona and California which have been introduced.

Daily Diet for Turkeys

14g cracked corn, milo or wheat.

14g Turkey Grow ration (24 per cent protein).

14 g choice of chickweed, fresh chopped alfalfa, swiss chard, comfrey, New Zealand spinach, carrot tops, chopped hydroponic grass (oats, barley—7 day).

5 g mealworms, crickets or grasshoppers.

14g berries: eugenia, pyracantha, strawberries, cherries or grapes.

5g Trout Chow.

Free choice oyster shell (hen-size).

Daily Diet for Turkey Poults

5g Game Bird Starter Crumble.

5g Trout Chow mixed with Crumble.

5g hard-boiled egg: *yolk only*.

5g greens: fine chopped lettuce, dandelion leaves.

*5 g insects: mealworms, crickets, roaches or corn-ear worms.

5g minerals: Vionate multivitamin powder, sprinkled on greens.

* 6–7 worms fed three times daily during first four weeks. When five weeks old, poults begin eating starting mash, trout chow, green food. At eight weeks, growing mash replaces starting mash.

Quails, Partridges and Francolins

The quails, partridges and francolins are grouped together for convenience as all have similar habits and diets, although they are diverse in distribution in the New and Old Worlds.

Typical of the New World quails is the popular Bob-white Quail (*Colinus virginianus*), 24 cm in length. These small chunky birds and their cheery whistles are familiar throughout the eastern and central USA and south into southern Mexico. They become very tame and often feed near homes. Pine woods, brushy fields and abandoned corn fields provide natural habitat for this quail.

They live in coveys of a dozen or more birds. At night the covey sleeps on the ground in a tight circle, heads out, tails in. Pairs are formed in the breeding season in the spring and territories are established. The nests are made in thick cover, fence rows and often in high grass. The nests are well made with an arch of woven grass over the top. Fourteen to sixteen white eggs usually form the clutch. The incubation is twenty-one days. The hens incubate the eggs and both sexes brood and care for the young. The chicks grow rapidly and can fly in two or three weeks. Insects, seeds, buds, small fruits, grass and snails all find a place in their diet.

In the western USA, the California Valley Quail (*Lophortyx californicus*), 23.5 cm in length, is familiar in suburban gardens and city parks. The male is identified by the bold black and white face patterns and a black, tilting plume. Both sexes have graceful plumes or crests on the head. They live in groups of fifteen to sixty birds. At night they roost in thickets or trees. This quail feeds chiefly on green vegetation and seeds, with insects comprising only about 3 per cent of its diet.

Nests are made in depressions in the ground, well-hidden and lined with grass. Nine to fourteen blotched, cream-white eggs are laid. The incubation period is twenty-one to twenty-two days. Both sexes incubate the eggs, brood and care for the chicks. Natives of the humid Pacific coast, they range from Oregon to Lower California. They have been introduced into the Hawaiian Islands, New Zealand, Vancouver Island, Washington and Colorado as game birds. They prefer open woodlands, chaparral and grassy valleys.

The Mountain Quail (*Oreortyx pictus*) which is 27.5 cm in length is the largest and most striking quail in North America. The chestnut throat, grey breast, barred flanks and long straight crest make them 'aristocrats' among quail. They prefer thick brush and mountain areas. This species is not found in large coveys, six to twelve birds making a normal grouping.

Nests are made near fallen logs or by rocks under bushes. Eight to twelve reddish-buff eggs are laid. The incubation period is twenty-four days. Both sexes incubate, brood and care for the young. There are thirty-three species of New World quail found from Canada to Argentina. None of the New World quail are migratory.

Old World quail, partridges and francolins have ninety-five species within their group. Many are migratory. They lack the cutting serration on the upper mandible which is found in New World quails. Most have spurs on the legs. Spurs are not present in the New World quail.

The Japanese Coturnix Quail (*Coturnix japonica*) is 20 cm in length. It has been domesticated by the Japanese and now large numbers are raised as egg producers. Pickled eggs for gourmet salads and dressed quail for table use has developed into a mammoth commercial enterprise in many countries. This sandy-brown, mottled with black, quail may lay 200 eggs in a single year when forced for production.

The Chinese Painted Quail (*Excalfactoria chinensis*) is only 15 cm in length, the smallest and perhaps the most beautiful of the quails. It is a native of south-eastern Asia, India, Sri Lanka, Indo-China and Taiwan. This miniature quail is colourfully marked with blue and chestnut and has a black and white bib. Other races are found in the Philippine Islands, Australia, Java, Borneo, Sumatra and Africa. Six to eight eggs, olive in colour and spotted with brown, form a normal clutch. The incubation period is sixteen days. The female incubates the eggs and both sexes feed and care for the chicks. Nests are made on the ground under clumps of tall grasses. The chicks are the size of bumble bees when hatched. They grow rapidly due to their rich, insectivorous food and mature at three months of age.

Daily Diet for Bob-white, Valley, Mountain and Scaled Quail

Seed: 5g milo, millet or canary.
Greens: 5g chickweed, dandelion, sow thistle or dock.
Insects: 5g mealworms or crickets.
Egg: 14g hard-boiled egg, crumbled (usually $\frac{1}{4}$ egg).
Trout Chow: 5g, mixed with seeds.
Minerals: 5g grit or oyster shell (hen-size).

Daily Diet for Japanese Coturnix Quail

Seeds: 5g millet or canary.
Greens: 5g chickweed or lettuce, grated finely.
Insects: 2 to 4 mealworms.
Egg: 14g hard-boiled egg, crumbled.
Trout Chow: 5g pellets, finely ground.
Minerals: $\frac{1}{2}$ tsp Vionate powder sprinkled on egg, also fine grit should be available.

The daily diet for Chinese Painted Quail is the same as for Japanese Coturnix.

The daily diet for quail chicks up to seven days of age should be fed three times daily and is: 5g turkey starter meal; 2g hard-boiled egg crumbled on the meal; 1 or 2 mealworms. No grit or greens should be offered before seven days of age.

The partridges and francolins are slightly larger birds. None are migratory and all are regarded as sporting birds. As a group, they eat seeds, berries, leaves and bulbs. This is supplemented by insects and grubs, particularly when chicks are being raised. The Chukar Partridge

(*Alectoris chukar*) is 32.5 cm in length and the European or Hungarian Partridge (*Perdix perdix*) is 30 cm in length. These have both been introduced into the United States and Canada as game birds.

Chukars are handsome birds, between the quail and grouse in size. They are easily recognized by their black striped face and barred flanks. The bill, feet and legs are bright red in colour. They need semi-arid open, rocky country and have done well in parts of the western USA where adequate water is available. Natives of the Indian Himalayas, they prefer to roost on the ground among rocky terrain.

Flocks of ten to forty birds are common. Nests are made in hollows near bushes or among rocks. Nine to twelve eggs may be laid. They are speckled buff-brown in colour. The incubation period is twenty-three days. Both sexes incubate, brood and care for the chicks. At four months of age the young look just like the parents. Chukars feed mainly on weed seeds, wild fruits, leaves and bulbs. They dig the bulbs out with the bill. Grasshoppers are probably their favourite insectivorous food.

The Hungarian Partridge or Hun originated in the cultivated fields of Eurasia. It ranges from the British Isles to the Caspian Sea. In the western USA and Canada it is important as a game bird. Partridges eat animal and plant food. Thirty-seven per cent of their food consists of insects. They live in heaths and moorlands and cultivated fields in the lowlands. Well planted aviaries are necessary for partridges in captivity.

Nests are made in growing corn fields, along fence rows and in windbreak areas. Nine to twenty eggs may be laid each season. The hen alone incubates the eggs for a period of twenty-four days, while the male guards the nesting site. Both sexes brood and feed the chicks. Sexes are alike in colouration. The crown is brown, streaked with buff. The body plumage is barred and striated with reddish brown. The breast is grey, marked with irregular lines of black and chestnut. The Hungarian partridge has an inverted chestnut horseshoe on the lower breast in both sexes.

The Crested Green Wood Partridge (*Rollulus roulroul*) is a most beautiful Indonesian wood partridge. It is 30 cm in length. This resident of the Malay Peninsula and Borneo lives on seeds, berries and insects. The male has an erect, fan-shaped crest, reddish brown in colour. The female has no crest. Both sexes are rich green in colour with chestnut wings.

Nests are made on the ground out of grasses and are roofed over. There is a side entrance. Four or five white eggs are laid. The incubation period is seventeen to eighteen days. The female incubates the eggs alone. Both sexes brood and feed the chicks when hatched.

The Chinese (Formosan) Bamboo Partridge (*Bambusicola thoracica*), 27.5 cm in length, is another small partridge often seen in captivity. The neck and head are chestnut brown, the back olive-brown, mottled and striated with buff, white and black. The cheeks, throat and sides of the head are a rich reddish brown. The eye stripe and breast are grey. The legs are spurred only on the male. The tail is rather long. A native of China, this bird has been introduced into Japan.

Nests are made on the ground of grass and twigs. Three to seven rufous coloured eggs, with fine brownish-red dots, are laid. The incubation period is eighteen days. The hen incubates the eggs and both sexes brood and feed the chicks.

The francolins are fairly large-sized game birds of Africa and Asia. Thirty-four species live in Africa and five in western and southern Asia. They inhabit steppes, savannahs, forests and mountains. All are vociferous and their voices may be heard at great distances. The legs are strong with one or two spurs in the males. The tail is short and rounded, with fourteen tail feathers. In many species, the sexes are similar in colour, although a few differ. Grain, seeds, berries, buds, insects and small invertebrates are eaten.

Nests are made on the ground between grass tussocks and are lined with grass stalks. Six to eight light brown or olive eggs, with white chalky spots, are laid. Incubation ranges from twenty-one to twenty-three days. The female alone incubates the eggs. Both sexes brood and feed the chicks.

Daily Diet for Chukar (*Alectoris chukar*) and Hungarian (*Perdix perdix*) Partridges

Grain or seeds: 5 g cracked corn, milo, wheat or millet.

Fruits or berries: 5 g, choice of tomatoes, figs, dates, melons, grapes, eugenia, pyracantha, cotoneaster, blackberries, raspberries, mulberries.

Game Bird F & M Chow: 14 g.

Choice of greens: 9 g sow thistle, spinach, dock, New Zealand spinach, comfrey, dandelion, swiss chard, hydroponic grass (7-day oats, barley).

Insects: 5 g mealworms (6 to 10), crickets or grasshoppers.

Minerals: free choice oyster shell (hen-size).

Daily Diet for Crested Green Wood Partridge (*Rollulus roulroul*)

Grain or seeds: 5 g canary or millet seed.

Fruits or berries: 5 g, choice of tomatoes, figs, dates, melons, grapes, eugenia, pyracantha, cotoneaster, blackberries, raspberries, mulberries.

Greens: 9 g chickweed or dandelion greens.

Insects: 3 or 4 mealworms.

Minerals: oyster shell (chick-size).

Daily Diet for Chinese (Formosan) Bamboo Partridge (*Bambusicola thoracica*)

5 g canary or millet seed.

9 g chickweed seed, dandelion greens or lantana blossoms.

3 or 4 mealworms.

Minerals: oyster shell (chick-size).

Daily Diet for Francolins

Seed or grain: 5 g canary, millet, milo, cracked corn, wheat.

Fruits or berries: choice of 5 g tomatoes, grapes, figs, dates, prunes, melons, eugenia, pyracantha, cotoneaster, blackberries, raspberries, mulberries.

Game Bird F & M Chow: 14g.

Greens: 9 g—choice of swiss chard, New Zealand spinach, sow thistle, dock, comfrey, hydroponic grass (7-day sprouted), oats or barley.

Insects: 5 g mealworms (6 to 10), crickets, grasshoppers or corn worms.

Hard-boiled egg: $\frac{1}{2}$ crumbled on F & M Chow.

Oyster shell: 5 g (hen-size).

The above diet may be used for Indian Black Francolin (*Francolinus francolinus asiae*), Grey (*Francolinus pondicerianus*), Sharpe's (*Francolinus clappertoni sharpi*), Erckel's (*Francolinus erckelii*) or Gray's Bare-throated (*Pternistes leucoscepus*).

Gruiformes

Cranes

Among the most spectacular of the groups of birds are the fourteen species of cranes in the family Gruidae. Possibly no group is more in need of protection. Their numbers have been sadly depleted during the last century, and at least six species are now seriously endangered. Cranes are found around the world except in South America, the Malayan Archipelago, the Pacific Islands and New Zealand. The cranes inhabit open marshlands, wet plains and prairies, sandy flats, and seashores.

They are long-legged, long-necked wading birds with thin legs and beaks. When flying, the neck is extended straight out. The plumage is black and white, white, grey or brown, with both sexes being alike. The voice is loud, since the windpipe or trachea is greatly developed and convoluted like the coils of a trumpet.

Both the Japanese Sacred Crane and the Whooping Cranes have spectacular courtship dances, full of grace and beauty.

All of the cranes are ground nesters, building bulky nests of vegetation in marshy areas, frequently surrounded by water. The normal clutch of eggs is two (sometimes three). The eggs are white or olive in colour, spotted or streaked with rich shades of brown. Incubation varies from twenty-eight to thirty-five days. Both parents share the duties of building the nest, incubating the eggs, and caring for the chicks. Chicks can walk and run a few hours after hatching. They are covered with reddish-brown down or greying down when hatched. They grow rapidly and at ten to twelve weeks of age are able to fly short distances.

Cranes breed well in captivity and some excellent diets have been formulated by nutritionists at US Wildlife Research stations and at State Universities so that the propagation of cranes under controlled conditions can take place. The Whooping Crane (*Grus americana*) and the Japanese Sacred Crane (*Grus japonensis*) have been saved from becoming extinct due to good husbandry.

Daily Diet for Crane Chicks (Hour Feedings)

Ground corn: 5g (1 tsp).

Purina Pellet Developer: 2g ($\frac{1}{2}$ tsp), moistened with water.

Dog Food: 2g Alpo canned chicken (fine) (or any canned pet food fortified with vitamins and minerals).

Trout Chow: 2g moistened with water.

Shredded lettuce: 2g.

Insects: 2g mealworms or crickets.

2g hard-boiled egg yolk, crumbled.

2g steamed bone meal.

Crane chicks are fed with a small syringe or eye-dropper when first hatched. A baby spoon may also be used with a very small amount being offered at each feeding. When chicks are hungry, they will 'peep' and call similar to baby chicks. Do not force food into the crane chick at any feeding unless the crop is completely empty.

One tsp of water is given in a spoon after each feeding.

Trumpeters

The three species of trumpeters are found in the family Psophidae. They are sociable, rain-forest birds, nesting in low tree stumps and feeding on insects and fallen fruits. All are velvety-black with white, grey or brown wing feathers.

Their length is 48 cm, their height 46 cm, and their weight may reach 1 kg. Pheasant-sized, they have long legs and necks, short fowl-like bills and small heads. The male has a loud trumpeting voice and this bird is the ventriloquist of the bird world. All are exceptionally tame and they make delightful pets. They roost in trees, so perches must be provided in aviaries if trees and shrubs are absent.

Daily Diet for all Trumpeters

Grain: 28g cracked corn.

Fruit: 14g (eugenia berries, grapes, raisins, blackberries, cotoneaster berries, diced tomato, apple or pears).

Hard-boiled egg (grated—58g).

28g ZuPreem or canned dog food.

$\frac{1}{2}$ slice bread (14g).

Mealworms or crickets: 5g.

Mouse: 20g.

Daily Diets for Cranes

Species	Choice grains (g)	Game bird pellets 30% protein (g)	Trout Chow (g)	Fish (g)	Meat (g)	Rodents (g)	Oyster shell
Whooping Crane (Grus americana)	227-corn, wheat, milo	113	28	40-anchovy (2)	28-ground	20-mouse	Free choice
Japanese Sacred Crane (Grus japonensis)	227-corn, buckwheat	113	28	40-anchovy	28-ground	20-mouse	Free choice
Sandhill Crane (Grus canadensis)	227-corn, wheat	113	28			40-mice	Free choice
European Crane (Grus grus)	227-wheat	113	28			40-mice	Free choice
Hooded Crane (Grus monacha)	113-wheat	56	28	20-anchovy, cut in 1-cm pieces	14-crickets		Free choice
White-naped Crane (Grus vipio)	227-wheat, rice	113	28	40-anchovy or carp		20-mouse	Free choice

Demoiselle Crane (*Anthropoides virgo*)	113	56			14-crickets	Free choice
Stanley (Blue) Crane (*Anthropoides paradisea*)	227-wheat, corn, milo	113	28		14-crickets, grasshopper	Free choice
Wattled Crane (*Grus carunculatus*)	227-wheat, milo	113	57	40-anchovy	20-mouse	Free choice
West African Crowned Crane (*Balearica pavonina*)	227-milo, wheat	113	57		14-crabs, grasshopper	Free choice
South African Crowned Crane (*Balearica regulorum*)	227-milo	113	57		14-crabs, grasshopper	Free choice

Rails

The rail family is by far the largest and most diverse of the order Gruiformes. All of the 132 species are small to medium-sized birds which are running, wading or swimming birds. Most are marsh inhabitants. Some live in wet forests, reedy streams and ponds and a few even in dry fields.

Rails, coots and gallinules have been placed in the family Rallidae. The coots and gallinules are simply rails which have become specialized for existence in a particular habitat. The coots have lobate-webbed toes adapted for walking on aquatic plants. Frontal shields are found on the forehead of both coots and gallinules.

Nests are made of grass and aquatic vegetation, well-hidden near water. The eggs, eight to fifteen in number, are white or buff in colour, spotted with brown or maroon spots. Both parents share the incubation duties and care of the young. The chicks are covered with black or brown down. They leave the nest soon after hatching and begin feeding the same day they are hatched.

Some of the rails are sparrow-sized and even the largest gallinule is only the size of a chicken. Many breed well in captivity in covered aviaries which have adequate water and are densely planted.

Daily Diet for all Rails

Meat: 5 g, sprinkled with Vionate multivitamin powder.
Hard-boiled eggs: 5 g (grated).
Seed: 5 g millet or canary seed.
Greens: 5 g, choice of chickweed, watercress, lettuce.
Bread: 2 g (cubed).
Insects: 5 g mealworms or crickets.

Sunbittern

The Sunbittern (*Eurypyga helias*), beautiful bird of Central and South America, is placed in a family, Eurypygidae, by itself. This bird ranges from southern Mexico to Peru and central Brazil, living in wooded edges of streams and ponds. It is 50 cm in length, with broad wings and long tail. The bill is long, thin and snake-like. The legs and toes are long. The plumage is soft, variegated and mottled with rich colours, resembling butterfly wings when the wings are extended. It is graceful when walking

Daily Diets for Coots and Gallinules

Species	Choice grain (g)	Meat (g)	Egg (g)	Bread (g)	Greens (g)	Oyster shell
American Coot (Fulica americana)	113-milo, wheat, cracked corn	28 minced	57 grated	28 (1 slice)	42.5	Free choice
Giant Coot (Fulica gigantea)	113-milo, wheat, cracked corn	28 minced	57 grated	28	42.5	Free choice
Red-knobbed (Crested) Coot (Fulica cristata)	113-milo, wheat, cracked corn	28 minced	57 grated	28	42.5	Free choice
Purple Gallinule (Porphyrula martinica)	113-milo, wheat, cracked corn	28 minced; 1 mouse	57 grated	28	42.5	Free choice
White-breasted Waterhen (Amauromis phoenicurus)	113-milo, wheat, cracked corn	28 minced; 1 mouse	57 grated	28	42.5	Free choice
Australian Swamphen (Porphyrio porphyrio)	113-milo, wheat, cracked corn	28 minced; 1 mouse	57 grated	28	42.5	Free choice
Common (Grey) Moorhen (Gallinula chloropus)	113-milo, wheat, cracked corn	28 minced; 1 mouse	57 grated	28	42.5	Free choice

[73]

and stalking its insectivorous prey. The bird is a picture of slow motion. When alarmed, it flies into trees. The nest is placed in low trees and is lined with mud. Two grey eggs form a clutch. Incubation and care of the young is shared by both parents. The food consists of small fish, crustaceans, frogs, insects, seeds and leaves.

Daily Diet for Sunbitterns

Meat: 28 g (minced, sprinkled with Vionate multivitamin powder).
Smelt: 17 g.
Insects: 5 g mealworms or crickets.
Egg: 28 g, grated.
Seed: 5 g millet or canary seed.
Greens: 7.5 g shredded lettuce or watercress.

Seriemas

The two species of seriemas in the family Cariamidae are the Crested (Red-legged) Seriema (*Cariama cristata*), 90 cm in length and 85 cm high, and the smaller Black-legged Seriema (*Chunga burmeisteri*), 78 cm in length and 58 cm in height. Both are greyish-brown in colour, long-legged running birds with crane-like posture. They both have strong down-curved bills, long necks, short wings and long tails. The Crested Seriema lives in the open grassland and pampas. The Black-legged Seriema lives only in brushy forested areas. Seriemas stalk their prey in a stately manner, feeding on rodents, reptiles, berries and insects. Both species roost in trees. Nests are made of sticks, placed in low trees or on the ground.

Two eggs, white with brown spots and streaks, form a clutch. Both sexes incubate the eggs and care for the young. The incubation period is twenty-four to twenty-six days. Both species are still common in their native habitat and are protected because of the snakes, mice and large insects they destroy. They will both breed in captivity if aviaries are large and well planted and if diets are complete.

Daily Diet for Seriemas

Meat: 28. g ground meat *or* ZuPreem Bird of Prey.
Rodents: 40 g mice.

Berries: 28 g eugenia, guava, cotoneaster, blackberry or blueberry.
Insects: 3 g mealworms or crickets.
Egg: 57 g crumbled, hard-boiled.

Bustards

The Bustards are a well-marked family, Otidae, of upland ground birds that live on open grassy plains, semi-desert, and brushlands. Twenty-three species may be found in Africa, Eurasia and Australia. Some are migratory, following the large populations of flying locusts and the ripening grain.

The Pygmy Bustard (*Otis tetrax*) of the Mediterranean area and temperate Asia, measures 42.5 cm in height. In contrast, the Great Kori Bustard (*Ardeotis kori*) of eastern and southern Africa measures 137 cm in height. All are ground birds and do not perch in trees. Camouflage colours of mottled brown, black and grey help these birds to hide. They remain motionless rather than running or flying when in danger. These birds have a bulky look, with long necks, and legs outstretched. Their food consists of grasshoppers, beetles, fruits, berries, grains, mice and small birds.

Bustards lay their one or two eggs on the ground. The eggs are reddish-brown or olive-green in colour. Incubation takes twenty-one days in the smaller forms and thirty days in the largest forms. The chicks are covered with mottled brown or black down. Twenty-four hours after hatching the chicks are foraging for food. They grow rapidly and at the age of six to eight weeks are able to fly.

Bustards have been hunted as game birds in many countries as the meat is delicious. Overshooting and destruction of habitat are blamed for their decreasing numbers. Bustards will breed in captivity. Breeders should be challenged to raise large numbers in captivity so that importation of wild stock will no longer be necessary.

(See table on p. 76.)

Daily Diets for Bustards

Species	Meat (g)	Rodents (g)	Hard-boiled egg (g)	Fruit (g)	Insects (g)	Grain/game bird pellets (g)	Oyster shell (g)
Great Kori Bustard (*Ardeotis kori*)	28-ground meat *or* ZuPreem Bird of Prey sprinkled with Vionate multiple vitamin	80-mice	57	14-figs, grapes, guava, tomato	3-mealworms, crickets	57-wheat, cracked corn, mixed 1/1 with Purina Game Bird Startena	Free choice
Australian Bustard (*Ardeotis australis*)	28-ground meat *or* ZuPreem Bird of Prey sprinkled with Vionate multiple vitamin	80-mice	57	14-figs, grapes, guava, tomato	3-mealworms, crickets	57-wheat, cracked corn, mixed 1/1 with Purina Game Bird Startena	Free choice
Black Korhaan (*Afrotis afra*)	28-ground meat *or* ZuPreem Bird of Prey diet	20-mice	28	14-figs, eugenia, grapes, raisins	7-mealworms, crickets	28-milo, wheat, mixed 1/1 with Purina Game Bird Startena	Free choice
Pygmy Bustard (*Otis tetrax*)	28-ground meat *or* ZuPreem Bird of Prey	20-mice	28	14-figs, eugenia, grapes, raisins	7-mealworms, crickets	28-milo, wheat mixed 1/1 with Purina Game Bird Startena	Free choice

Charadriiformes

GULLS · TERNS · PLOVERS · LAPWINGS · THICK-KNEES ·
STONE CURLEWS · SANDPIPERS · AVOCETS · STILTS ·
OYSTERCATCHERS

There are sixteen families in this order. They are principally waders, swimmers and divers, inhabiting the inland marshes, lakes and coastal waters, beaches and meadows of the world.

Gulls and Terns

The eighty-two species of gulls and terns are world-wide in distribution except for continental Antarctica. These waterbirds range in size from 20 to 60 cm.

Gulls are useful scavengers, removing trash and debris left by irresponsible individuals on our beaches.

White, grey and black plumage is found in both gulls and terns. Long, pointed wings, short legs, webbed feet, stout hooked bills and square tails identify the gulls. Terns are smaller, with slender bodies, straight pointed bills and forked tails. Normally, terns are white with grey backs or black wing tips. Gulls soar frequently to locate food, swim well and pick up food from the surface of the water as on land. Terns usually dive for minnows, do not soar, and swim poorly.

Most of these birds nest colonially on the ground, the gulls making bulky, untidy piles of grass, seaweed and twigs for nests. Two or three eggs are usual, olive or buff grey in colour, blotched with brown. Both sexes incubate and attend the chicks which can swim at the age of seven to ten days.

Terns usually nest on sand, depositing three eggs in a depression or small hollow dug out with their feet. The eggs are white, olive or cream coloured, marked beautifully with brown or black spots and streaks.

Gulls must be the easiest of all birds to feed in captivity as they will eat almost anything that is offered. Terns are more difficult to keep in good health and most species do not live long in captivity.

Daily Diets for Gulls and Terns

Species	Meat (g)	Hard-boiled egg (g)	Fish, squid (g)
Great Black-backed Gull (*Larus marinus*)	227-ground, sprinkled with Vionate *or* ZuPreem Bird of Prey Diet	28	227-mackerel or 227'-squid
Black-headed Gull (*Larus ridibundus*)	113-ground, srinkled with Vionate	28	40-choice of anchovies, sardines, whitebait, smelt, herring
California Gull (*Larus californicus*)	Identical diet		
Ring-billed Gull (*Larus delawarensis*)	Identical diet		
Bonaparte's Gull (*Larus philadelphia*)	Identical diet		
Silver Gull (*Larus novaehollandiae*)	Identical diet		
Inca Tern (*Larosterna inca*)			60-whitebait fish or sardines
Caspian Tern (*Sterna caspia*)			60-whitebait fish or sardines

Plovers, Lapwings, Thick-Knees and Stone Curlews

The seventy-two species of plovers, lapwings, thick-knees and stone curlews are worldwide in distribution except for Antarctica. They range in size from 15 to 58 cm. They are wading and running birds with short, thick necks, long wings and short tails. The hind toe is absent. Adults are patterned in grey, brown, gold, black and white. The sexes are alike.

Their food consists of shellfish, other marine invertebrates, insects, snails, lizards and small rodents. They have pigeon-like bills that are shorter than the head.

Plovers all nest in inconspicuous depressions in the sand or ground. Eggs number two to four, olive or buff in colour and blotched with brown. They are pear-shaped. The plovers are celebrated for their 'broken wing' act to lure intruders away from their nests. This behaviour may be observed in aviaries as well as in the wild. Some, like the thick-knees and stone curlews, are nocturnal. Many migrate long distances. The

Daily Diets for Plovers, Lapwings and Thick-knees

Species	Meat (g)	Hard-boiled egg (g)	Insects (g)	Seeds (g)	Trout Chow (g)	Boiled rice (g)
Golden Plover (Pluvialis dominica)	5-ground or 5-canned salmon	28	5-mealworms, crickets, earthworms	5-rape, millet, canary	5-mixed w/meat	14
Killdeer (Charadrius vociferus)	5-ground	28	5-mealworms, crickets, earthworms	5-rape, millet, canary	5-mixed w/meat	450 mg
Egyptian Plover (Pluvialis aegyptus aegyptus)	5-ground or 5-canned salmon	28	5-mealworms, crickets	5-rape, millet	5-mixed w/meat	14
Blacksmith Plover (Vanellus armatus)	Identical diet					
Lapwing Plover (Vanellus vanellus)	Identical diet					
Australian Thick-knee (Southern Stone Curlew) (Burhinus magnirostris)	5-ground 20-mouse	28	14-mealworms, crickets	5-milo, millet	5-mixed w/meat	14

Note : Feed seed in one pan; all other food in second pan in 2.5 cm of water.

Golden Plover (*Pluvialis dominica*) migrates 3860 km (2400 miles) from Nova Scotia to South America. The reason for these movements is still not understood.

Sandpipers

The eighty-two species of sandpipers are wading birds of the family Scolopacidae. They are readily distinguished from the plovers by their thin straight or down-curved bills. World-wide in distribution, they are absent only in the Antarctic regions. Their plumage is mainly dull grey, buff or brown, mottled or streaked. It is possible to identify many by their tail, rump and wing markings. Some are upland birds, others freshwater, but most are seen along ocean shores where they feed on molluscs, crustaceans, insects, seeds and small invertebrates. They are often seen in flocks. Their voices are varied with trills, harsh calls and alarm notes. All possess a hind toe except one species, the Sanderling.

In size, they range from 13 to 64 cm. Like other shorebirds, most nest on the ground. The exceptions are the European Green Sandpiper and the American Solitary Sandpiper. Among the pests which they eat are grasshoppers, army worms, cutworms, cabbage worms, cotton worms, boll weevils, rice weevils, Texas fever ticks, horseflies and mosquitos. This makes them very valuable to mankind.

Their eggs number from two to four, olive or buff in colour, with dark markings. The female incubates the eggs and both sexes share in feeding the young. The chicks are covered with soft downy feathers and leave the nest a few hours after hatching, accompanying the parents in search of food.

Avocets and Stilts

The avocets and stilts are a small family, Recurvirostridae, consisting of seven species. They are found in temperate and tropical regions of most of the world, inhabiting open marshes or wet grasslands near fresh, brackish or salt water. Spectacularly patterned with black and white plumage, they are medium-large (38 cm), slender-legged wading birds. Their long bills, curved upward in the avocets, straight in the stilts, skim the surface of ponds and bays for insects and their larvae. Diving beetles, grasshoppers and bill-bugs which feed on corn are eaten in large numbers by both species.

Daily Diets for Sandpipers

Species	Meat (g)	Hard-boiled egg (g)	Insects (g)	Boiled rice (g)	Fish (g)	Seeds (g)	Trout Chow (g)	Steamed Bone meal (g)
Western Sandpiper (*Calidris mauri*)	5 minced	14	5-meal-worms or crickets	5	5-canned salmon or chopped fish	5-millet or aquatic grass seeds	5 mixed w/meat	5 and 1 tsp salt
Spotted Redshank (*Tringa erythropus*)	5 minced	14	5-meal-worms or crickets	5	5-canned salmon or chopped fish	5-millet or aquatic grass seeds	5 mixed w/meat	5 and 1 tsp salt
European Ruff (*Philomachus pugnax*)	5 minced	14	5-meal-worms or crickets	5	5-canned salmon or chopped fish	5-millet or aquatic grass seeds	5 mixed w/meat	5 and 1 tsp salt

Note : Feed in 2.5 cm of water in small stainless steel pan.

Avocets feed freely on water snails and marine worms as well. They sweep the water with their bills. Stilts probe in mud with their straight bill.

Both nest on the ground, on islands or in marshes. The nest is made of grasses and weed stems. Three or four eggs are laid normally. The eggs are pale olive or buff coloured, thickly spotted and blotched with dark brown. Incubation and rearing of the chicks is shared by both parents.

Daily Diet for Stilts

Minced meat: 14 g.
Trout Chow: 14 g, mixed with meat.
Insects: 5 g mealworms or crickets.
Egg: 14 g, hard-boiled, crumbled.
Boiled rice: 5 g.
Shrimp: 5 g, powdered.
Fish: 5 g, chopped or ground.
Steamed bone meal: 5 g.

The daily diet for avocets is the same—*except* that they should receive 9 g of insects.

Oystercatchers

The six species of oystercatchers in the family Haematopodidae are large, conspicuous, noisy, plover-like birds. They are seen on open beaches and rocky coasts throughout the world, except in the polar regions and some oceanic islands. They range from 37.5 to 400 cm in length. They differ from all other pied shorebirds in that they have long orange or red bills and stout pink legs. Their outstanding feature is their long, blunt, vertically flattened knife-like bill. With this powerful tool, oystercatchers can chisel limpets off the rocks and open oysters, mussels and clams easily. They also use this strong bill to kill small crabs and to probe into mud for worms.

Two major colour patterns predominate: either sooty-black body colours, or bold pied brown or black above and white below. Broad white wing patches may be seen in flight. The call note is a loud, shrill whistle which carries for some distance. The call is repeated as the birds run rapidly along the beach or when alarmed while flying.

The European Oystercatcher (*Haematopus ostralegus*) feeds on hundreds of lugworms (*Arenicola marina*) found on shoals. Shore crabs, marine snails, and mussels are also eaten.

In North America, the American Oystercatcher (*Haematopus palliatus*) feeds on oysters along the coast of North Carolina. When the banks are freshly flooded and the shells of molluscs are open a crack, the oyster-catcher inserts its beak into this crack and prises it open. Many shellfish are also eaten.

Nests may be on open beaches and are often decorated with white shells, pebbles and debris. Two to four eggs are usually laid. The eggs are yellowish in colour and blotched with brown and black streaks. Both parents share in incubation duties and care of the chicks. The young are able to run as soon as they are dry after hatching. Secretive and wary, they are difficult to see.

Daily Diet for Oystercatchers

28 g of ground meat.
57 g of fresh shrimp.
20 g chopped sardines (2.5-cm pieces).
5 g (1 tsp) Trout Chow mixed with the meat.
28 g boiled rice.
57 g clams, razor or pismo.

Columbiformes

DOVES · PIGEONS

There are few individuals in the world who are not familiar with some kind of pigeons or doves. There are 284 species with 716 geographical races and forms in the family Columbidae. Pigeons and doves vary in size from 15 to 88 cm in length. The names 'pigeon' and 'dove' are interchangeable terms, the larger forms called pigeons and the smaller forms called doves.

World-wide in distribution in the temperate and tropical regions, these birds are heavily concentrated in the warmer parts of the New World. In a few remote oceanic islands and the vast belt between the sub-Arctic and the Arctic, pigeons and doves are missing.

Despite their great variety in colour, size and habits, all members of the pigeon family are so distinctly pigeons that they are easily recognized as such. All are stout-bodied birds with short necks and small heads. All have short, slender, rounded bills, thickening towards the tip and thinner in the middle, with a flashy cere at the base through which the nostrils emerge.

Most pigeons and doves are strong fliers. The coat of sturdy-shafted feathers must be handled or touched with care since the feathers are loosely attached to the skin and drop out easily. All drink like horses, immersing the bill in water, sucking up the water without raising the head to swallow.

Compared with passerine birds, pigeons and doves have a limited range of vocalizations. Cooing calls are monotonous, repeated many times. The whistling calls of the green pigeons (*Treron* sp.) are more interesting. The deep booming calls of the large Goura Pigeons of the rain forests are pleasing to the human ear. Squabs or chicks use a squeaking call to let the parents know that they need feeding.

The pigeon family is uniform in its nesting habits. The nests are usually flimsy platforms of sticks and leaves. They are placed in trees, on the ground, in holes in trees or in burrows. They are sometimes found on cliff ledges and on the roofs of buildings. One or two white or buff-coloured eggs are laid. Incubation periods have been recorded from fourteen to twenty-eight days. Both sexes incubate the clutch of eggs and feed the young.

Both parents feed the chicks with 'pigeon milk', predigested food. As the parent birds incubate, the lining of the crop thickens, and when the chick or squab hatches, the lining of the crop breaks off into a cheesy curd which the adults regurgitate into the young. This 'pigeon milk' has much the same food value as mammals' milk. To obtain this food, the young poke their beaks inside the mouth of the parent birds. After two weeks of this early feeding, the young are fed half-digested seeds and berries from the crop. The squabs grow rapidly and leave the nest three or four weeks after hatching. Most pigeons and doves rear several broods each year.

The majority of pigeons and doves live on vegetable food. Seeds, grains and fruits are favourite items of their diet. Several species do eat insects, worms, grubs and snails. All show a strong liking for salt and other minerals.

The pigeons and doves fall naturally into three groups; the seed-eating pigeons and doves of both the Old and New Worlds, the fruit pigeons of Africa, Australia, Asia and the East Indies and the giant Crowned Pigeons of New Guinea and adjoining islands.

The seed-eating pigeons include not only the typical pigeons but many smaller forms called doves. The largest populations are ground birds, little specialized in their feeding habits. Nuts, small fruits, buds, insects and grubs are eaten with the seeds and grains.

Daily Diet for Domestic Pigeon and Rock Pigeon (Rock Dove) (*Columba livia*)

Grain: 14 g each of corn, wheat, milo maize and peas.
Choice of greens: 28 g swiss chard, comfrey, vetch or clover.
Bread: 42 g whole wheat (1 slice).
Purina Pigeon Chow Checkers: free choice.
Minerals: 14 g grit, oyster shell or dry snails (crumbled).

Daily Diet for Wonga-wonga Pigeon (*Leucosarcia melanoleuca*) and Band-tailed Pigeon (*Columba fasciata*)

14 g each of milo, peas and wheat.
Choice of greens: 28 g swiss chard, comfrey or vetch.
Bread: 23 g whole wheat bread.
Purina Pigeon Chow Checkers: 28 g.
Minerals: 14 g oyster shell, grit, crumbled egg shells.

Daily Diet for White-crowned Pigeon (*Columba leucocephala*)

Grain: 14 g each milo maize and field peas.
Choice of greens: 28 g swiss chard or comfrey.
Bread: 23 g whole wheat bread.
Purina Pigeon Chow Checkers: 28 g.
Minerals: 14 g oyster shell or crumbled egg shells.

Daily Diet for Bronze-winged Pigeon (Common Bronzewing) (*Phaps chalcoptera*)

Grain: 14 g each milo maize, brown rice and canary seed.
Greens: 28 g spinach.
Bread: 23 g whole wheat bread.
Insects: 2 g mealworms.
Minerals: 14 g oyster shell.

Daily Diet for Nicobar Pigeon (*Caloenas nicobarica*)

Grain: 14 g each milo maize, wheat and hemp.
Greens: 28 g swiss chard or kale.
Bread: 23 g whole wheat bread.
Minerals: 14 g oyster shell.

Daily Diet for Bleeding Heart Pigeon (*Gallicolumba luzonica*)

Grain: 14 g each of milo maize, canary seed and millet.
Greens: 28 g choice of chickweed or watercress.
Bread: 23 g whole wheat bread.
Insects: 2 g mealworms.
Purina Pigeon Chow: 5 g.
Minerals: 14 g oyster shell.

Daily Diet for Barbary (Ringed) Turtle Dove (*Streptopelia risoria*)

Grain: 14 g each milo maize, canary seed and millet.
Greens: 28 g chickweed or lettuce.
Bread: 23 g whole wheat bread.
Insects: 2 g mealworms.
Purina Pigeon Chow: 5 g.
Minerals: 14 g oyster shell or crumbled dry egg shell.

Daily Diet for Chinese Spotted Dove (*Streptopelia chinensis*)

Grain: 14g each milo maize, canary seed and millet.
Greens: 28g chickweed.
Minerals: 14g oyster shell, medium size.
Bread: 23g whole wheat bread.

Daily Diet for Diamond Dove (*Geopelia cuneata*)

Grain: 14g each millet, canary seed and rape.
Green: 28g chickweed or clover.
Purina Pigeon Chow: 5g.
Minerals: 14g oyster shell, chick-size.

Daily Diet for Galapagos Ground Dove (*Zenaida galapagoensis*)

Grain: 14g each millet, canary seed and rape.
Greens: 28g chickweed or spinach.
Bread: 11g whole wheat bread ($\frac{1}{4}$ slice).
Insects: 2g mealworms.
Purina Pigeon Chow: 5g.
Minerals: 14g oyster shell, chick-size.

Daily Diet for Peaceful Dove (Barred Ground Dove) (*Geopelia striata*); Mourning Dove (*Zenaida macroura*); and White-winged Dove (*Zenaida asiatica*)

Grain: 14g each milo maize, canary seed and millet.
Greens: 28g chickweed.
Minerals: 14g oyster shell.

Daily Diet for: Javan Orange-breasted Green Pigeon (*Treron bicincta javana*); Bruce's Yellow-bellied (Green) Pigeon (*Treron waalia*); West African Green Pigeon (*Treron australis*); Philippine Pink-necked Pigeon (*Treron vernans*); Thick-billed Green Pigeon (*Treron curvirostra*); Cloven-feathered Fruit Pigeon (*Drepanoptila holosericea*); White-eared (Lesser) Brown Fruit Dove (*Phapitreron leucotis*) and Black-chinned Green Fruit Dove (*Ptilinopus leclancheri*)

Fruits and berries: 14g fresh figs, banana, papaya, guavas, blueberry, mulberry, and blackberry (mixture of any).
Canned fruit cocktail: 28g.
Boiled rice: 14g (fed in separate, small dish).

[87]

Hard-boiled egg: 28g, mixed with boiled rice.
Trout Chow: 5g, mixed with boiled rice.

Daily Diet for Pied Imperial Pigeon (*Ducula bicolor*); Imperial Fruit (Green Imperial) Pigeon (*Ducula aenea*); and Pacific Fruit Pigeon (*Ducula pacifica*)

Choice of fruits: 14g figs, palm fruit, apricots, plums, cherries, black-berries, raspberries, mulberries, eugenia, raisins.
Vegetables: 28g boiled sweet potato or boiled carrots.
Hard-boiled egg: 28g, crumbled, mix with bread and milk.
Bread and milk: 14g.
Trout Chow: 5g, mix with bread and milk.

Daily Diet for Crowned Pigeons

Choice of grain: 14g corn, wheat or milo maize.
Choice of greens: 21g swiss chard, comfrey or lettuce.
Fruits and berries: 72g diced bananas, papaya, apple, grapes, raisins (soaked overnight in water), figs, eugenia, mulberry, raspberry, blue-berry (mixture of any).
Bread: 43g whole wheat bread.
Insects: 5g mealworms.
Nuts: 7g peanuts.
Fruit cocktail: 76g canned fruit cocktail or diced fruit.
Oyster shell: free choice (hen-size).
Garden snails: 2.

The above diet is used for Blue-crowned (Common Crowned) Pigeon (*Goura cristata*), Sheepmaker's Crowned Pigeon (*Goura scheepmakeri scheepmakeri*), Sclater's Crowned Pigeon (*Goura scheepmakeri sclaterii*), Insular Crowned Pigeon (*Goura cristata minor*), Victoria Crowned Pigeon (*Goura victoria victoria*) and Beccari's Crowned Pigeon (*Goura victoria beccarii*).

The following diet is used for hand-feeding Crowned Pigeon chicks: 5g banana; 5g bread and milk; 2 Theralin capsules (multivita-mins); and one capsule of Dicalcium Phosphate in the morning and another in the evening. The Theralin and Dicalcium Phosphate capsules are available from Lamb Laboratories, Nashville, Tennessee (P.O. Box 11672, postal zone 37211). In the UK, a substitute for Theralin capsules is available from poultry laboratories, and Dicalcium Phosphate capsules or Calcium Glutonate are available in health food shops.

Psittaciformes

MACAWS · COCKATOOS · PARROTS · PARAKEETS ·
LORIES · LOVEBIRDS

The family of parrots, Psittacidae, consists of over 317 kinds, with many geographical forms. Parrots are most abundant in Australasia and the tropical New World. Central and South America, Africa, Asia, Malaya, the Malagasy Republic, Australia and New Zealand provide homes for this interesting family. In size, they range from the pygmy parrots (10 cm in length) to the giant Hyacinthine macaws (100 cm in length).

Besides the true parrots, many special names have been given to the smaller groups: macaws, cockatoos, cockatiels, parakeets, budgerigars, rosellas, lovebirds, lories, lorikeets, amazons and pygmy parrots. The common body colour in most species is green, but all colours of the rainbow may be found, with contrasting patches of red, yellow, blue, violet, white and black on the head, wings, legs and tail.

The strong hooked beak and the feet, with two toes in front and two behind, identify most parrots and their relatives. Their small eyes are often bordered with patches of bare skin. This is seen in macaws and cockatoos. The tongue is thick and fleshy in many parrots, fringed and brush-tipped in the lories and lorikeets. With few exceptions the sexes are alike in colouration.

Typically they are forest birds, feeding on nuts, seeds, fruits, berries, nectar of flowers, insects and larvae.

Nests are made in holes and hollows in trees, in termite mounds, in burrows and in sandbanks. One parrot, the Quaker (Monk) Parakeet (*Myiopsitta monachus*) of South America, builds a bulky stick nest like a haystack. The eggs, one to eight, are always white in colour. Chicks are helpless when first hatched, with eyes closed. The incubation, brooding and feeding of chicks is shared by both sexes.

Parrots only develop their ability to mimic and speak in captivity. Young birds learn to speak more easily than older birds. They learn by hearing the words or phrases in repetition and great patience is required in teaching them. The African Grey Parrot (*Psittacus erithacus*) of central Africa must be considered the finest speaking parrot and has a soft modulated voice. In the wild, all are raucous-voiced birds that squawk, shriek and chatter with a poor range of vocal expression.

More species of parrots have been raised in captivity than any other group of birds. Their brilliant colouration, their speaking ability, affection to each other, reaction to flattery and ability to use their feet as hands have made them popular household pets.

Balanced diets have developed through research of their nutritional problems. New breeding records are being established each year with several of the endangered species.

Daily Diets for Macaws

Purina Dog Chow: 14 g.

Choice of seed: 14 g corn, wheat, milo maize or safflower.

Nuts: 14 g choice of almonds, walnuts, hickory nuts, pine nuts, Brazil nuts. *Peanuts, with one drop of wheat germ oil placed in opened end should be fed during the breeding season.*

Fruit: 37.5 g choice of banana, orange or apple—cut in pieces.

Vegetables: 18 g fresh corn on the cob—14 g carrots or sweet potato.

Greens: 21 g swiss chard, comfrey, New Zealand spinach or hydroponic pieces of sprouted oats.

Free choice oyster shell (hen-size) or crumbled, dried chicken egg shells.

The above diet is used for: Hyacinthine Macaw (*Anodorhynchus hyacinthinus*); Lear's Macaw (*Anodorhynchus leari*); Blue and Yellow Macaw (*Ara ararauna*); Red and Yellow (Scarlet) Macaw (*Ara macao*); Military Macaw (*Ara militaris*); Green-winged (Red and Green) Macaw (*Ara chloroptera*); Golden-naped Macaw (*Ara auricollis*); and Chestnut-fronted Macaw (*Ara severa*).

Daily Diet for Cockatoos

Purina Dog Chow: 14 g.

Seeds: 14 g choice of sunflower, wheat, milo, oat groats, eucalyptus seed, melaleuca seed (bottlebrush bush).

Nuts: 14 g peanuts or almonds.

Fruit: 37.5 g choice of orange or apple cut in quarters.

Vegetables: 18 g fresh corn on the cob, carrots or sweet potato.

Greens: 21 g swiss chard, New Zealand spinach, comfrey, dock, spinach or hydroponic sprouted oats.

Free choice of oyster shell (hen-size) and cuttlefish bone.

Note: 11 g whole wheat bread is fed to all cockatoos. See also page 202.

The above diet is used for: Leadbeater's (Major Mitchell's) Cockatoo (*Cacatua leadbeateri*); Greater Sulphur-crested Cockatoo (*Cacatua galerita*); Citron-crested Cockatoo (*Cacatua sulphurea citrinocristata*); Roseate Cockatoo (Galah) (*Cacatua roseicapilia*); Slender-billed Cockatoo (Long-billed Corella) (*Cacatua tenuirostris*); Bare-eyed Cockatoo (Little Corella) (*Cacatua sanguinea*); Great White Cockatoo (*Cacatua alba*); Salmon-crested Cockatoo (*Cacatua moluccensis*).

Diet for Gang Gang Cockatoo (*Callocephalon fimbriatum*)

Purina Dog Chow: 14 g.
Seeds: 14 g choice of sunflower, safflower, wheat, oat groats, eucalyptus, melaleuca, acacia, banksia, casuarina and pine.
Nuts: 14 g peanuts, pinenuts or almonds. (One drop of wheat germ oil is placed in end of peanuts during breeding.)
Fruits: 37.5 g apple (cut in quarters), eugenia, hawthorn, pyracantha, cotoneaster berries, mulberries or hakea.
Greens: 21 g swiss chard, comfrey, spinach, beets or hydroponic sprouted oats or barley.
Free choice of gastropods, marine snail shells dried and crumbled.

Daily Diet for: Red-tailed Black Cockatoo (*Calyptorhynchus magnificus*); Yellow-tailed Black Cockatoo (*Calyptorhynchus funereus*), White-tailed Black Cockatoo (*Calyptorhynchus baudinii*) and Great Black (Palm) Cockatoo (*Probosciger aterrimus*)

Seeds: 14 g choice of sunflower, safflower, wheat, oat groats, eucalyptus, melaleuca, acacia, banksia, casuarina and pine, corn on cob.
Purina Dog Chow: 14 g.
Nuts: 5 g macadamia, peanuts or almonds.

The fruit of the Pandanus Screw Pine is fed to the Great Black Cockatoo.

Note: 11 g whole wheat bread is fed to all cockatoos.

Daily Diet for Amazons

Purina Dog Chow: 14 g.
Seeds: 14 g choice of corn, sunflower, safflower, oat groats, milo maize.
Nuts: 14 g choice of peanuts, pine, almond. One drop of wheat germ oil should be placed in each peanut in breeding season.
Fruit: 37.5 g apple, oranges, bananas (cut in pieces).

Greens: 21 g choice of spinach, dock, dandelion, swiss chard, comfrey, or hydroponic oats or barley (7-day old).

Corn on the cob: 18 g (fresh).

Vegetables: 18 g sweet potato or carrots in 2.5-cm pieces.

Cuttlefish bone: free choice.

The above diet is used for: Blue-fronted Amazon (*Amazona aestiva*); Finsch's Amazon (Lilac-crowned Parrot) (*Amazona finschi*); Orange-winged Amazon (*Amazona amazonica*); Spectacled Amazon (White-fronted Parrot) (*Amazona albifrons*); Green-cheeked Amazon (Red-crowned Parrot) (*Amazona viridigenalis*); Panama Yellow-fronted Amazon (*Amazona ochrocephala panamensis*); Yellow-naped Amazon (*Amazona o. auropalliata*); Double Yellow-headed Amazon (*Amazona o. oratrix*); and Single Yellow-headed (Yellow-fronted) Amazon (*Amazona ochrocephala*).

It should be noted that 11 g of whole wheat bread is fed to all amazons daily.

Daily Diet for Eclectus Parrot

Seed: 14 g choice of sunflower, safflower, wheat, corn on cob (fresh).

Fruits: 37.5 g choice of fresh figs, papaya, orange, apple, grapes, banana, pears.

Berries: 5 g choice of blueberries, blackberries, hawthorn, mulberries, eugenia or pyracantha.

Vegetables: 18 g cooked sweet potatoes or carrots in 2.5-cm pieces.

Purina Dog Chow: 5 g.

Nuts: 14 g choice of peanuts, pine nuts, almonds. One drop of wheat germ oil is placed in opened end of peanuts during breeding season.

Cuttlefish bone: free choice.

The above diet is used for Grand Eclectus Parrot (*Eclectus roratus roratus*); Cornelia's Eclectus Parrot (*Eclectus r. cornelia*); Red-sided Eclectus Parrot (*Eclectus r. polychloros*) and Solomon Island Eclectus Parrot (*Eclectus r. solomonensis*).

Daily Diet for Hawk-headed (Red-fan) Parrot (*Deroptyus accipitrinus*)

Seed: 14 g choice of sunflower, boiled maize, rice, millet sprays, safflower or oat groats, corn on cob (fresh).

Fruit: 37.5 g choice of banana, figs, papaya, cherries, grapes or guavas.

Vegetables and greens: 18 g grated carrots and choice of spinach, dock, chickweed, calendula buds, New Zealand spinach.
Purina Dog Chow: 5 g *or* Mynah pellets.
Nuts: 28 g peanuts, almonds or pine nuts (shelled).
Rice: 5 g.
Cuttlefish bone: free choice.

Daily Diet for Pesquet's Parrot (*Psittrichas fulgidus*)

Fruit: 37.5 g choice of papaya, figs or guavas.
Vegetable: 18 g cooked sweet potato with one leaf of shredded spinach, dock, swiss chard or chicory.
Mynah Bird Pellets: 5 g *or* Trout Chow may be used.
Egg: ½ hard-boiled, mixed with pellets.
Nuts: 28 g peanuts, with one drop wheat germ oil added in each nut.
Boiled rice: 5 g with one teaspoon corn syrup.
Cuttlefish bone: free choice.

Daily Diet for Black-headed Parrot (*Pionites melanocephala*)

Seed: 14 g choice of sunflower, corn on cob, boiled maize or oat cereal.
Fruits: 37.5 g choice of apples, guavas, eugenia berries or redcurrants.
Greens: 18 g chickweed, sour dock, watercress or dandelion.
Nuts: 28 g walnuts (cracked).
Trout Chow: 5 g.
Insects: 10 mealworms.
Bread: 11 g whole wheat with two drops of wheat germ oil.
Cuttlefish bone: free choice.

Daily Diet for Lesser Vasa (Black) Parrot (*Coracopsis nigra*)

Seed: 14 g choice of sunflower, oat groats, corn on cob or boiled rice.
Fruits: 33 g choice of apple, guava, eugenia, pyracantha or mulberries.
Greens: 18 g choice of carrot tops, dandelion, chickweed, comfrey, spinach or dock.
Insects: 5 mealworms.
Nuts: 28 g choice of peanuts, almonds or grated coconut.
Bread: 5 g with two drops wheat germ oil.
Cuttlefish bone: free choice.

Daily Diet for African Grey Parrot (*Psittacus erithacus*)

Seed: 14 g choice of sunflower, boiled maize, corn on cob or oat groats.
Fruits: 37.5 g bananas, oranges and apples.
Greens: 18 g spinach, dock, swiss chard, hydroponic oats.
Trout Chow: 5 g.
Nuts: 28 g choice of peanuts, almonds.
Bread: 5 g with two drops wheat germ oil.
Cuttlefish bone: free choice.

Daily Diet for Senegal Parrot (*Poicephalus senegalus*)

Seeds: 14 g choice of sunflower, kaffir corn, canary, millet, safflower, millet sprays (soaked).
Fruit: 37.5 g choice of cherries, plums and apples.
Greens: 18 g choice of twigs of willow, ash, hawthorn, acacia blossoms, sow thistle or chickweed.
Nuts: 28 g hazelnuts, peanuts, almonds, or locust beans.
Bread: 11 g whole wheat.
Vegetable: 18 g boiled carrots.
Cuttlefish bone: free choice.

Daily Diet for Philippine (Blue-crowned) Racquet-tailed Parrot (*Prioniturus discurus*)

Rice: 14 g, boiled.
Fruit: 37.5 g choice of papaya, pear, figs, guavas, blueberries *or* canned fruit cocktail or diced fruits.
Greens: 18 g chickweed or dandelion.
Purina Dog Chow: 5 g.
Insects: 5 mealworms.
Bread: 11 g whole wheat.
Vegetable: 18 g boiled sweet potato.

Daily Diet for Barraband's Parakeet (Superb Parrot) (*Polytelis swainsonii*)

Seed: 14 g choice of sunflower, canary, millet, wheat, oat groats, acacia and eucalyptus seed or corn on the cob.
Fruit: 37.5 g apples, eugenia or lantana berries.
Greens: 18 g choice of chickweed, comfrey, swiss chard or carrot tops.
Bread: 11 g whole wheat.
Cuttlefish bone: free choice.

Daily Diet for Rock Pebbler Parakeet (Regent Parrot) (*Polytelis anthopeplus*)

Seeds: 14 g choice of sunflower, wheat, canary, millet, oat groats, eucalyptus seed, corn on the cob.
Fruit: ¼ apple.
Greens: 18 g choice of chickweed, sour dock, New Zealand spinach, hydroponic sprouted oats (7-day).
Bread: 11 g whole wheat.
Cuttlefish bone: free choice.

Daily Diet for King Parakeet (*Alisterus scapularis*)

Seeds: 14 g sunflower, wheat, oat groats, safflower, corn on the cob.
Fruits: 37.5 g apple or orange in small pieces or eugenia berries.
Nuts: 28 g peanuts.
Mynah Bird Pellets: 5 g.
Bread: 11 g whole wheat bread.
Vegetable: 18 g soy beans, sweet potato.
Cuttlefish bone: free choice.

Daily Diet for Crimson-winged Parakeet (*Aprosmictus erythropterus*)

Seed: 14 g choice of acacia, grevillea, sunflower, wheat, canary, oat groats, or corn on the cob.
Fruit: 37.5 g ¼ apple, and choice of guavas, eugenia berries.
Greens: 18 g New Zealand spinach, sow thistle or chickweed.
Nuts: 28 g peanuts or shelled almonds.
Insects: 5 mealworms.
Bread: 11 g whole wheat bread.
Cuttlefish bone: free choice.

Daily Diet for Maroon Musk Parrot (*Prosopeia tabuensis*)

Seeds: 14 g choice of sunflower, milo maize, corn on the cob.
Fruits: 37.5 g choice of bananas, figs, guavas, apples (¼).
Greens: 18 g New Zealand spinach or chickweed.
Nuts: 2 peanuts.
Purina Dog Chow: 5 g.
Vegetable: 18 g boiled sweet potato.
Bread: 11 g whole wheat bread.
Cuttlefish bone: free choice.

Daily Diet for Derbyan Parakeet (*Psittacula derbyana*)

Seeds: 14 g choice of sunflower, wheat, oat groats, corn on the cob.
Fruit: ¼ apple.
Greens: 18 g New Zealand spinach or hydroponic sprouted oats or wheat (7-day).
Nuts: 2 peanuts.
Purina Dog Chow: 5 g.
Vegetable: 18 g raw carrots.
Bread: 11 g whole wheat bread.
Cuttlefish bone: free choice.

Daily Diet for Kea Parrot (*Nestor notabilis*)

Seed: 14 g sunflower, wheat, corn on the cob.
Fruit: ¼ apple.
Greens: 18 g hydroponic sprouted wheat or oats or ½ head lettuce.
Nuts: 2 peanuts.
Purina Dog Chow: 5 g or 5 g Trout Chow.
Vegetable: 5 g green peas.
Bread: 11 g whole wheat bread.
Cuttlefish bone or quail mineral block: free choice.

Daily Diet for: Many-coloured Parakeet (Mulga Parrot) (*Psephotus varius*); Blue-bonnet Parakeet (*Psephotus haematogaster*); Hooded Parakeet (*Psephotus dissimilis*); Golden-Shouldered Parakeet (*Psephotus chrysopterygius*); Bourke's Parakeet (*Neophema bourkii*); Scarlet-chested (Splendid) Parakeet (*Neophema splendida*); and the Elegant Parakeet (*Neophema elegans*)

Seeds: 5 g choice of canary, millet, millet sprays, oat groats or thistle seeds.
Greens: 18 g choice of chickweed, sow thistle, lantana blossoms, calendula buds, groundsel, dandelion, shepherd's purse or sweet alyssum.
Fruits and berries: 5 g diced apple, cotoneaster or pyracantha berries.
Insects: 5 to 10 mealworms.
Bread: 11 g whole wheat bread with two drops wheat germ oil added.
Minerals: charcoal, 5 g; or cuttlefish bone.

Daily Diet for Indian Ring-neck Parakeet (*Psittacula krameri manillensis*)

Seeds: 14 g sunflower, wheat, oat groats, or corn on the cob.
Fruit: ¼ apple or pear.
Greens: 18 g hydroponic sprouted oats or barley or spinach, dock or swiss chard.
Nuts: 2 peanuts.
Purina Dog Chow: 5 g.
Vegetable: 5 g green peas.
Bread: 11 g whole wheat bread.
Cuttlefish bone or quail mineral block: free choice.

Daily Diet for: Port Lincoln Parakeet (*Barnardius zonarius*); Eastern Rosella (*Platycercus eximius*); Pale-headed Rosella (*Platycercus adscitus*); Northern Rosella (*Platycercus venustus*); Green Rosella (*Platycercus caledonicus*); Crimson Rosella (*Platycercus elegans*); Western Rosella (*Platycercus icterotis*): Red-rumped Rosella (*Psephotus haematonotus*) and Quaker (Monk) Parakeet (*Myiopsitta monachus*)

Seeds: 14 g choice of wheat, sunflower, millet, corn on the cob, eucalyptus or acacia seeds and blossoms, oat groats.
Fruits: 37.5 g choice of apple, guavas or grapes.
Greens: 18 g choice of sow thistle, New Zealand spinach, swiss chard, hydroponic sprouted oats or wheat, chickweed, silver beet or lantana blossoms.
Insects: 2 g mealworms.
Nuts: 28 g peanuts or almonds.
Purina Dog Chow: 5 g.
Bread: 11 g whole wheat.
Minerals: 5 g charcoal; cuttlefish bone—free choice.

Daily Diet for Turquoise Parakeet (*Neophema pulchella*)

Seeds: 5 g millet, canary, hulled oats, millet sprays or thistle seed.
Greens: 18 g choice of chickweed, dandelion, sow thistle, groundsel, shepherd's purse, sweet alyssum, lantana blossoms.
Fruits or berries: 5 g diced apples, cotoneaster berries.
Insects: 2 g mealworms.
Bread: 11 g whole wheat.

Wheat germ oil: 2 drops on bread.
Minerals: 5 g charcoal, cuttlefish bone.

Daily Diet for Swift Parakeet (*Lathamus discolor*)

Seeds: 5 g canary, hulled oats or hemp.
Greens: 18 g eucalyptus or acacia blossoms, lantana blossoms.
Pound cake: 11 g with 5 g Karo syrup (golden syrup) diluted half
with water and poured over cake.

Daily Diet for Red-fronted Parakeet (*Cyanoramphus novaezelandiae*)

Seeds: 5 g canary, millet, hulled oats or hemp.
Greens: 18 g chickweed, sow thistle, New Zealand spinach, sweet alyssum or dandelion.
Fruit: 5 g diced apple, pear or hawthorn or pyracantha berries.
Insects: 5 mealworms.
Bread: 11 g whole wheat.
Wheat germ oil: 2 drops on bread.
Cuttlefish bone: free choice.

Daily Diet for Budgerigar (*Melopsittacus undulatus*)

Seeds: 5 g mixed 2 parts canary seed to 1 part millet, millet sprays, oat groats.
Greens: 18 g choice of chickweed, dandelion, shepherd's purse, sweet alyssum, New Zealand spinach, chicory, or hydroponic sprouted oats (7-day).
Bread: 11g whole wheat.
Cuttlefish bone, mineralized grits or block.

Daily Diet for Cockatiel (*Nymphicus hollandicus*)

Seeds: 5 g canary, millet, hulled oats or sunflower.
Greens: 18 g chickweed, swiss chard, comfrey, dandelion, sweet alyssum, sow thistle or New Zealand spinach.
Fruit: $\frac{1}{4}$ apple.
Bread: 11 g whole wheat.
Minerals: 5 g cuttlefish bone, mineralized block, grit.

Cockatiels should receive 5 g pound cake each day during the breeding season.

Daily Diet for Vernal (Indian) Hanging Parrot (*Loriculus vernalis*) and Philippine Hanging Parrot (*Loriculus philippensis*)

Nectar: 9 g of nectar made from 5 g oyster milk, 9 g white sugar, 5 g condensed milk, 5 g Karo syrup (corn syrup) or golden syrup, 9 g breadcrumbs, 3 g orange-flavoured halibut-oil baby drops.

Fruit: 5 g chopped papaya, diced apple, pears, grapes and figs.

Insects: 2 g mealworms.

Blossoms: 5 g honeysuckle or lantana.

Vitamins and minerals: 2 g ABDEC multivitamin supplement or any good multivitamin supplement; contents of one dicalcium capsule (1 g); 1 g fine bone meal.

Seeds: 5 g canary, millet, and 2 g rape seed.

Daily Diet for: Golden (Queen of Bavaria's) Conure (*Aratinga guarouba*); Sun Conure (*Aratinga solstitialis*); Petz's Conure (Orange-fronted Parakeet) (*Aratinga canicularis*); Golden-crowned Conure (Peach-fronted Parakeet) (*Aratinga aurea*); Black-headed or Nanday Conure (*Nandayus nenday*); Thick-billed Parrot (*Rhynchopsitta pachyrhyncha*); and the Greater Patagonian Conure (*Cyanoliseus patagonus*)

Seeds: 5 g sunflower, maize, canary, hulled oats, corn on the cob.

Greens: 18 g sow thistle, New Zealand spinach, swiss chard, chicory, comfrey or hydroponic sprouted oats or barley (7-day).

Fruit: 37g choice of apple, orange, mango, papaya or guava.

Bread: 11g whole wheat.

Vegetable: 5 g carrots or soy beans.

Purina Dog Chow: 5 g.

Minerals: 5 g cuttlefish bone; free choice grit.

Nuts: 2 peanuts.

Daily Diet for Lories and Lorikeets

Fruit: 14 g papaya or apples on spikes; diced figs, grapes, apples, pears, raisins (soaked overnight in water) *or* canned fruit cocktail or diced fruits with 5 g corn syrup added to whole can of fruit.

Bread or boiled rice: 5 g.

Evaporated milk: 5 g.

Karo syrup: 2 g.

Vegetables: 2g grated carrots and lettuce (half and half).

[99]

Minerals: 2 g cuttlefish bone meal.

Vitamins: 3 g Vionate multivitamin powder *or* ABDEC multivitamin supplement.

Note: All food is mixed together in a soupy consistency and fed in one pan.

The above diet is fed to: Black Lory (*Chalcopsitta atra*; Red Lory (*Eos bornea*); Red-collared Lorikeet (*Trichoglossus haematodus ribritorquis*); Yellow-backed Lory (*Lorius garrulus flavopalliatus*); Blue-crowned Lory (*Vini australis*); Stella's Lorikeet (*Charmosyna papou stellae*); Musk Lorikeet (*Glossopsitta concinna*); and Rainbow Lory (*Trichoglossus haematodus moluccanus*).

Daily Diet for Lovebirds (*Agapornis*)

Seed: 5 g milo, canary, millet, hulled oats, millet sprays, acacia or sunflower.

Greens: 14 g choice of chickweed, sow thistle, dandelion, spinach, dock, New Zealand spinach, swiss chard, comfrey, lantana blossoms, shepherd's purse, groundsel or hydroponic sprouted oats or barley (7-day).

Minerals: 5 g cuttlefish bone, mineral block or mineral grit.

Berries: 5 g pyracantha, cotoneaster or eugenia berries.

Bread: 11 g whole wheat bread.

The above diet is used for Peach-faced Lovebird (*Agapornis roseicollis*); Fischer's Lovebird (*Agapornis fischeri*); Nyasa Lovebird (*Agapornis lilianae*); Black-masked Lovebird (*Agapornis personata*); Black-cheeked Lovebird (*Agapornis nigrigensis*); Abyssinian (Black-winged) Lovebird (*Agapornis taranta*); Madagascar (Grey-headed) Lovebird (*Agapornis cana*) and Red-faced Lovebird (*Agapornis pullaria*).

Musophagiformes

TOURACOS

There are ten species of Touracos or 'Plantain-eaters' in the family Musophagidae. Beautiful forest birds, they are found only in Africa. They have colourful green, grey-brown, and blue bodies with red markings in the wings. The green and red colours of touracos are true pigments. The red pigment, Tuacin, a copper complex of Uroporphyrin III, can be extracted in laboratories by chemical means. It is used in human medicine for the treatment of kidneys and other internal organs.

They range from 37.5 to 75 cm in length. The wings are short and rounded. The bill is short, the head is small and usually crested. The tail is long. Non-migratory, these birds are usually seen in pairs or family groups. The flight is weak and dipping. Touracos climb vines and run along tree branches like squirrels. Some run fast on the ground. The feet and toes are well muscled with two toes in front and two behind like the cuckoos.

Most nest high in forest trees. A platform nest of sticks and twigs is constructed. Two or three white eggs form a clutch and they are unmarked. Both sexes incubate and feed the chicks on berries, fruits and insects, which are regurgitated. Chicks hatch in about seventeen days and are covered with sooty-grey down. They grow very fast and may leave the nest in about fourteen days. With their strong feet, they crawl out on nearby branches where the parents continue to feed them until they can be independent.

Touracos live well in captivity and are breeding in several collections where nutrition and facilities are favourable for propagation. Hartlaub's Touraco (*Tauraco hartlaubi*) of the highlands of Kenya and Tanzania, the Knysna Touraco (*Tauraco corythaix*) of South Africa, Lady Ross's Touraco (*Musophaga rossae*) of East Africa and the Great Blue Touraco (*Corythaeola cristata*) of the forest areas of Central Africa are favourites. All feed on fruits, berries, shoots and insects.

Daily Diet for Touracos

Fruits: 14 g choice of papaya, pear, apple, grapes, currants soaked overnight in water, mangoes, apricots, figs; *or* $\frac{1}{4}$ can fruit cocktail (diced fruits).

Berries: 14 g choice of eugenia, pyracantha, mulberries, blackberries, raspberries, loganberries, blueberries.

Insects: 5 g choice of crickets or mealworms.

Greens: 5 g choice of swiss chard, spinach, dock, chicory, watercress, parsley, sprouted oats.

Minerals: 1 g cuttlefish bone, steamed bone meal—sprinkled on greens.

Trout Chow: 5 g.

Bread and milk: 11 g with 2 drops wheat germ oil.

Cuculiformes

ROADRUNNERS

The Greater Roadrunner (*Geococcyx californianus*) is the best known of the thirteen species of ground-cuckoos. In this large (55 cm) terrestrial bird of the arid south-western USA the wings are short and rounded and the bill decurved. The black and amber plumage is coarse in texture. The tail is long and graduated, the feet are large and strong, and the head is crested.

The roadrunner is famed as a snake-killer—including rattlesnakes. It also eats mice, rats, young rabbits, ground squirrels, small birds, horned toads, lizards, scorpions, centipedes, snails, crabs, caterpillars, bugs, ants, bees, wasps, grasshoppers and crickets. This bird is a great runner and has been clocked at 15 miles per hour (24 kph).

A picturesque bird, it nests in cactus, yuccas, blue thorn and buckeye bushes or in low trees such as mesquite, cedar, live oak or hackberry. The nest is made of twigs about 30 cm in diameter and is well concealed in the centre of the cactus or bush. Four to six eggs are laid, white or pale yellow in colour. The incubation period is fourteen to seventeen days. Both sexes share the incubation and care of the chicks. As many as twenty baby mice may be fed to one growing chick each day. Because of their varied diet, roadrunners are easy to feed in captivity.

Daily Diet for Greater Roadrunner

Rodents: 80 g (4 mice, 1 chick, $\frac{1}{2}$ rat, $\frac{1}{2}$ ground squirrel).
Meat: 28 g ground meat or canned dog food.
Insects: 14 g grasshoppers, caterpillars or mealworms.
Egg: 1 hard-boiled, fed half in the morning and half in evening.
Vitamins: 5 g Vionate multivitamin supplement sprinkled on meat.

Strigiformes

Owls swallow their prey whole, and when the strong stomach juices have removed all the nutrients and indigestible bones, fur and feathers are formed into small pellets and ejected from the mouth. As owls hunt within a few miles of their roosting perches, these pellets may be counted, dissected and analysed to indicate the food eaten and the abundance of small animals in a particular territory.

The weird calls of owls are varied. Hooting, mewing, wailing, crying and barking sounds have been recorded. Soft musical trilling calls identify many of the smaller owls. Antiphonal duets occur in mated pairs.

Nests are made in burrows, on grassy plains, in trees, on cliff ledges, in cacti and in tree holes. They may also be found in buildings and the deserted nests of birds and squirrels.

The owl eggs are spherical in shape, white in colour and range in number from four to ten or more. Usually both parents incubate the eggs and in all species both parents feed the young.

Their tremendous range of food is most interesting: jack rabbits, cottontails, rats, mice, ground squirrels, skunks, chipmunks, snakes, frogs, lizards, scorpions, opossums, lemmings, fish, birds and insects.

The Java Fishing Owl (*Ketupa ketupu*) has small suction pads on the underside of its toes to prevent it slipping on wet rocks as it catches frogs and fish. The tiny Elf Owl (*Micrathene whitneyi*) of the south-western USA is only 14 cm in length. It feeds on scorpions and insects, removing the scorpion's stinger before swallowing. The Ferruginous Pygmy Owl (*Glaucidium brasilianum*) is 15 cm in length. It has been observed catching hummingbirds in Brazil.

Species	ZuPreem (g)	Poultry (g)	Rodents (g)	Fish Insects (g)	Natural food
Great Eagle Owl (*Bubo bubo*) (3200 g)	277	917-chicken 51-chick	400-rat 20-mouse		Hare, grouse, pigeon, magpie, coot, fish, frog
Great Horned Owl (*Bubo virginianus*) (1800 g)	277	51-chick	400-rat 20-mouse 850-guinea-pig		Skunk, hares, squirrel, ground squirrel
Java Fishing Owl (*Ketupa ketupu*) (450 g)	277	51-chick	20-mouse	80-anchovy	Fish, frogs
Long-eared Owl (*Asio otus*) (300 g)	28	51-chick	20-mouse		Moles, field mice, small birds, insects
Hawk Owl (*Surnia ulula*) (120 g)	28	51-chick 125-coturnix quail	20-mouse		Field mice, lemmings, weasels, small birds
Burrowing Owl (*Athene cunicularia*) (190 g)		51-chick 125-coturnix quail	20-mouse		Field mice, lizards, snakes, insects
Snowy Owl (*Nyctea scandiaca*) (2000 g)	277		400-rat 20-mouse		Lemmings, mice, rats, alpine hare, ptarmigan
Spectacled Owl (*Pulsatrix perspicillata*) (600 g)		51-chick 125-coturnix quail	850-guinea pig 400-rat 20-mouse		Spiny mice, crabs, wood rats, small birds, grasshoppers, caterpillars
Great Grey Owl (*Strix nebulosa*) (1000 g)	277	125-coturnix quail	400-rat 20-mouse		Field mice and bank voles, thrushes, small birds, moles, rats, mice
Elf Owl (*Micrathene whitneyi*)				5-mealworms 15-crickets (*Gryllus domesticus*)	Scorpions, flying insects, grasshoppers, hawk moths, beetles
Ferruginous Pygmy Owl (*Glaucidium brasilianum*) (15 g)		27-coturnix quail, one week old	20-mouse	5-mealworms 15-crickets	Small birds, mice, shrews, lizards, grasshoppers, beetles
Barn Owl (*Tyto alba*) (300 g)	277	51-chick	400-rat 20-mouse		Rats, mice, ground squirrels
Thailand Barn (Bay) Owl (*Phodilus badius*) (250 g)		51-chick 125-coturnix quail	20-mouse	5-mealworms	Small mammals, birds, frogs, lizards, large insects

Caprimulgiformes

FROGMOUTHS · NIGHTJARS

Comparatively little is known about the twelve species of nocturnal frog-mouths in the family Podargidae. They are found from Australia north to Malaysia and in the Philippine Islands east to the Solomon Islands. In many ways they resemble our New World Nightjars and Whipoorwills in appearance, but their manner of feeding is entirely different.

They feed on moths, beetles, centipedes, scorpions, caterpillars, mice and frogs. The nightjars and poorwills feed on the wing, catching large and small insects in flight. The frogmouths usually catch their prey on the ground, sitting quietly on a stump or a branch of a tree, then fluttering down on the prey.

They range from 22.5 cm to 52.5 cm in length. Their soft, silky plumage is owl-like, patterned with obscure streaks, battings and irregular fine lines. The frogmouths are a perfect example of cryptic camouflage when sitting on tree limbs or boughs. The entire plumage is greyish or ruddy brown. Their legs are very short and the feet are small and weak. The bill is large, flat, hooked, horny and triangular.

The Tawny Frogmouth (*Podargus strigoides*) of Australia has a large mouth and the lining of the mouth is a bright yellow. This colour attracts large flying moths at night when the mouth is opened and the moths fly right into the mouth and are eaten.

The sexes are alike in colour. These birds are day sleepers, perching lengthwise on horizontal branches with head up and eyes closed. In 1957, one of the authors was able to catch a sleeping pair in broad daylight with no difficulty.

Most frogmouths nest in the forks of horizontal branches. The nest is a frail platform of twigs, leaves, lichen and mosses which are prevalent in forested areas. Feathers are plucked from the female's breast and used to line the nest. Only one or two white eggs are laid. Both sexes incubate the eggs for the twenty-nine to thirty day period and both parents brood and feed the chick. The chicks are covered with long white downy feathers when hatched and are completely helpless and dependent on the parents for food.

Their nocturnal habits make them difficult to feed in captivity without unlimited facilities.

Daily Diet for Frogmouths (*Podargus strigoides*), hand-fed

Mice or rats: 3 new-born mice or rats fed, one each at 7 am, 12 noon and 6 pm.
Insects: sphinx moth (1–2) or crickets (2–3).
Leopard frog: 1 (133 g).
Snails: 1 (6 g), crumbled.
Vitamins: 1 g Vionate multivitamin powder sprinkled on rodents, frog and moths.

Daily Diet for Dusky Poorwill (*Phalaenoptilus nuttallii californicus*), hand-fed

Mice or rats: 3 new-born, fed one each at 7 am, 12 noon and 6 pm.
Insects: cockroaches (3–4) or crickets (2–3).
Vitamins: 1 g Vionate multivitamin powder sprinkled on rodents.

Daily Feeding Schedule for Frogmouth Chick

1 to 3 days old: 1 new-born mouse fed at 6.30 am, 1 pm and 5 pm.
3 to 8 days old: 1 new-born mouse fed at 6.30 am, 10 am, 1 pm and 6 pm.
8 to 12 days old: 1 new-born mouse fed at 7 am, 10 am, 1 pm and 2 at 5 pm.
12 to 19 days old: 2 small mice fed at 7 am, 1 small mouse fed at 10 am and 1 pm, and 1 new-born rat at 6 pm.
19 to 32 days old: 3 small mice fed at 7 am, a small mouse at 10 am and 1 pm and 1 new-born rat at 6 pm.

After thirty-two days, birds placed on adult diet.

Apodiformes

Hummingbirds

The western hemisphere's richest gift to the avian world is the fantastic family of Trochilidae. The 319 species of hummingbirds combine diminutive size with brilliant colours. Many species are cloaked in iridescent colours that are more dazzling in sunlight than those of the birds of paradise. Some species possess patches of iridescence on the breast or abdomen, others have a bright head patch or crown. Many males wear a bright bib.

The vibrant darting and hovering flight of hummingbirds requires up to eighty wing beats per second and demands the highest energy output of any warm-blooded creature. Hence, most hummingbirds need fifty to sixty meals a day. The smallest must eat every ten minutes during waking hours to survive. Their food consists of nectar, sipped by means of the long tongue, and insects, which they seek especially just before retiring in order to fortify themselves for the night. Vain, fearless, pugnacious, a hummingbird will fight constantly to defend its territory against trespassers as large as mockingbirds, orioles and jays.

Hummingbirds are found at many elevations with wide temperature variations. The family ranges from Tierra del Fuego, off southern South America, to Alaska. It is most abundant in the northern Andes mountains of South America. Hummingbirds live in every type of habitat. In the USA, the Ruby-throated Hummingbird (*Archilochus colubris*) is the only species in the entire area east of the Rocky Mountains. In the south-west, there are fourteen species. In California, the resident species are Anna's Rufous, Black-chinned, Costa's and Calliopes. All are colourful and attractive and are found from the coast to the desert.

Hummers capitalize on their small size and exceptional flying abilities to invade the world of flowers. They may gather nectar from 2,000 blossoms in one day. The wide availability of flowers from ground level to tree tops has encouraged an amazing diversification in form, structure and colour. Their tremendous energy is derived from the quick sugars in flower nectar. The proteins needed for growth come from small insects captured in these same flowers. While birds such as honeycreepers, sunbirds, flower-peckers, lories, warblers and tanagers of both hemispheres have adopted nectar feeding to supplement other diets, few live as exclusively on nectar, and none gather it entirely while in flight as do the hummers.

Our experience in keeping fifty-eight species of hummingbirds has shown that correct feeding is essential in maintaining these birds. Early efforts were only partially successful as the birds invariably succumbed after a short period. The problem was mainly nutritional, resulting from the use of diets composed entirely of sugar and honey solutions. The diets suggested in this book are diets formulated in conjunction with Dr Augusto Ruschi, the world's leading authority on hummingbirds. Dr Ruschi is director of the Museo Mello Leitao at Santa Teresa, Espirito Santo, Brazil. His thirty years of experience point out that a hummer's diet consists of 50 per cent nectar for heat and energy and 50 per cent insectivorous (protein) for growth and tissue repair. Dr Ruschi has propagated and raised sixty-one species of hummingbirds in his aviaries and has had several species live ten to twelve years in captivity.

We recommend a basic food of nectar, composed of cane sugar and Super Hydramin Powder, mixed with water and supplemented with vitamins and *Drosophila* (fruit flies). The solution is fed in glass feeders and is continuously available to the birds. The tip of the feeding spout is painted red with fingernail lacquer to attract the birds to the feeders. Red is the first colour of preference for most hummers.

Dr Ruschi demonstrated, through controlled studies in feeding, that *honey*, when consumed regularly by hummingbirds, leads to a fungus growth on the tongue, causing necrosis of the tissue. This results in a slow and painful death.

To attract the hummers, many persons add red food colouring to the nectar mixtures. This practice is not necessary if the tip of the feeder tube is painted red. Nutritionally, the food colouring has little value but, if preferred, it may be continued since that now on the market does not harm the birds.

Apart from nectar, hummingbirds require, as do all warm-blooded animals, proteins, fats, minerals and vitamins in their diet. Wild hummers catch large numbers of small flies, spiders and other tiny creatures which are found on flowering trees, shrubs, and plants in the western hemisphere. This protein must be provided when they are kept in captivity.

Daily Diet for Hummingbirds

1 quart water.
1 cup cane sugar.
1 teaspoon Hydramin Powder.
Mix thoroughly and place in feeders, which should be cleaned thoroughly
each time mixture is changed. Be sure no trace of detergent is left in
feeder.
Drosophila (fruit flies) should be released in the aviary at 8 am and
4.30 pm.

Writing in *Aviculture Magazine* (Vol. 68, No. 2, 1962), R. C. Lasiewski
presented alternate diets which he had used. Diet No. 1 was a sugar solution; 1 part sugar to 3 parts water, available at all times, and providing
a minimum of twenty *Drosophila* for each bird per day. His Diet No.
2 was a protein solution consisting of 1½ tablespoons Mellin's food (Hor-
licks Baby Cereal is an alternative), 1½ teaspoons Ledinac (Gevral Protein
Nutritional Supplement can be used), 3 teaspoons evaporated milk, 8
drops Vipenta (a multivitamin supplement—alternative: Albevita), 0.14
litres of granulated sugar and red food colouring with enough water added
to make 0.57 litres of this mixture, which was for the daytime. At night,
he used the Diet No. 1 solution. Both diets may be made in large batches
and kept refrigerated; however, if the evaporated milk formula is used,
the milk should be from a freshly-opened can as older milk will hasten
spoilage of the solution. The red food colouring is an indicator of spoilage
in the protein solution.

Mr Don Bleitz, of the Bleitz Wildlife Foundation, suggests the following diet: 2½ cups (557 g) sugar poured into 4 cups (907 g) hot water and
mixed thoroughly. This is poured into a 4.5-litre jar and cold water
added to fill the jar. Five drops of any good liquid multi-vitamin, water-
soluble, should be added to this solution and the liquid may be stored
safely in a refrigerator for one week. This solution provides only the
carbohydrates needed by the birds, together with some vitamin supple-
mentation. An adequate protein source is also necessary and is provided
by feeding *Drosophila* and/or other protein food.

Many species of hummingbirds, particularly the Sylphs, most Ama-
zilias, Colibri and all North American hummingbirds, will do well on
the sugar-water-vitamin nectar and the fruit-fly cultures. Some genera,
however, have proven almost impossible to keep in aviaries. These depend to a considerable extent upon plant pollen, particularly that of a
high altitude plant, *Chuquira acutiflora*, whose blossom resembles that

of an orange thistle. This provides a considerable portion of the amino acids, proteins and other nutritional factors for several species which live at high altitudes where insects and spiders are much less abundant due to the cold nights.

For a number of years certain genera of hummingbirds have been unsuccessful as aviary birds. Among these are the *Metallura*, *Eriocnemis*, some species of *Coeligena* and *Oreotrochilus*. This group needs a pollen supplement in its daily diet. After much experimentation, Mr Don Bleitz determined that the pollen containing the necessary requirements was carried on the legs of bees. A device for removing a part of this pollen as the bees entered their hives was developed by Mr Bleitz and his group, and the pollen is blended as to source to avoid pesticides and to ensure a constant protein value, and is packaged and kept refrigerated until use. Like other food products, it is perishable.

Only a small amount of pollen, 1 g, is needed to mix with 230 g sugar-water nectar. The pollen is mixed into a paste, with water, the paste is then mixed with additional water until all particles are thoroughly dispersed and then it is added to the regular water solution.

Hummingbirds will not live long in small cages. They should only be kept in a large aviary which simulates freedom. The aviary should have heavy planting and numerous flowering plants. Foggers or some sprinklers are necessary as all hummingbirds bathe and play in the water. The aviary should contain many feeding tubes, at least one feeder for every two or three birds. This avoids competition and fighting around the food source. The nectar should always be fresh, should be renewed frequently and the composition should always be the same. If the nectar is mixed in a haphazard fashion there are sure to be digestive disturbances and there could even be toxic poisoning.

Cliff Swallows

The seventy-nine species of swallows, in the family Hirundinidae, are world-wide in distribution except for the polar regions, New Zealand and a few oceanic islands. All are migratory.

They range in size from 10 to 23 cm. The wings are very long and pointed. The tail is cut short or forked. The legs are short and the feet are small and weak. Most bills are short and flat with stiff bristles at the base. The mouth gap is large and adapted for swallowing flying insects.

The plumage is compact with a metallic sheen on the upper parts. The sexes are alike in colouration.

Gregarious and well-liked by humans, they are completely insectivorous and spend most of their time devouring unwelcome insect life. They feed on the wing, eating mosquitoes, lawn moths, flies and tropical insects. Most swallows nest in colonies in hollow trees or rocks or in burrows dug in banks. Some build cone-shaped mud nests fastened to cliffs or under the eaves of buildings.

Four to seven white eggs, some speckled and spotted with reddish-brown and lilac are laid. Both sexes incubate the eggs and feed and care for the chicks.

The Cliff Swallow (*Petrochelidon pyrrhonota*) lives in large colonies. Its call is a single melodious note. It is distributed over most of North America. Mud-bottle nests are plastered on perpendicular rocks in many places, on the face of bluffs along rivers, under eaves of barns or houses. One of the most famous of the colonies in the west is that at Mission San Juan Capistrano. This group arrives in March of each year and departs in November, migrating to Mexico and Central America.

An analysis of the stomach contents of over 100 swallows showed that 39 per cent consisted of ants, bees and wasps. Assorted types of bugs made up 27 per cent of the contents and beetles formed 19 per cent. Of these, 17 per cent were harmful. Gnats, flies, mosquitos etc. completed the food eaten.

Swallows do not live well in captivity, either in small cages or in aviaries. Young birds are occasionally hand-reared and then released, as all efforts to teach swallows to pick up food from the ground have failed. Swallow chicks which have been orphaned or deserted may be raised on the following diet and then released when able to fly.

Daily Diet for Swallow Chicks

5 g (1 tsp) cottage cheese.
5 g (1 tsp) fresh egg yolk, mixed into cottage cheese.
2 g ($\frac{1}{2}$ tsp) grit, mixed with cottage cheese.
5 g (1 tsp) Vionate multivitamin powder, sprinkled in cottage cheese
   mixture and thoroughly mixed in.

Chicks are fed on a one-hour schedule with a teaspoon.

Coliiformes

COLIES (MOUSEBIRDS)

The coly (or mousebird) family is a small group of six species which is found only in Africa. They live in open country, brushland and forest edges. Sociable birds, they forage for buds, tender leaves, fruits, berries and insects. Farmers and fruit growers detest them because they eat so many fruits, being especially fond of figs. In South Africa the trees must be covered to prevent a complete loss of crops.

They range from 31.5 to 35.5 cm in length. The male and female are alike in their sombre tan or brown feathers and pink feet and legs. The name 'mousebird' refers to the soft, hairy-looking plumage on the breast and under-parts, as well as to the way they creep about, their bodies hugging the branches. They are slender-bodied with prominent crests. A long, stiff, pointed tail, consisting of ten feathers which are usually twice the length of the body, adds to their mouse-like appearance. Other characteristics are the presence of four notches on the breastbone, the absence of feathers around the oil gland and short, rounded wings. Oil from the oil gland is used for preening. They often run on the ground and are fond of dust bathing.

All four toes are directed forward, although the first or outer toe on each foot can be turned backward at will as the birds cling and climb with their sharp, curved toenails. Colies are acrobatic and comical. Using their feet and bills, they creep along branches like parrots. At night they sleep in pairs or in family groups in a more or less upright position with all four flexible toes hooked over the perch and the long tail hanging straight down.

The nests are either in a shallow cup of grass, lined with hair or wool or a platform of small twigs and leaves placed in trees or shrubs. Two or four white eggs, streaked with brown, are laid each year. Both sexes share the nesting duties and care for the chicks. The incubation period is fourteen days. The chicks are hatched naked but a sparse coat of downy feathers soon develops. Both parents feed the chicks with partially digested food by regurgitation. The chicks grow rapidly and move in and out of the nest at the age of two or three weeks, begging for food from the parent birds.

These are interesting birds to raise in aviaries, especially the Striated

(Speckled) Mousebird (*Colius striatus*) of central and south Africa, the Blue-naped Mousebird (*Colius macrourus*) of the dry belt below the Sahara, the Red-faced Mousebird (*Colius indicus*) of southern Africa and the White-headed Mousebird (*Colius leucocephalus*) of east Africa.

Daily Diet for Striated, Blue-naped, Red-faced and White-headed Mousebirds

Choice of fruit: 5 g (1 tsp) figs, dates, pears, grapes, raisins (soaked overnight in water), loquats, oranges, apples. Canned fruit cocktail or diced fruits may be used.

Choice of berries: 5 g blueberries, cranberries or eugenia.

Greens: 5 g lettuce.

Insects: 13 g mealworms (4–5), twice daily.

Vitamins: 5 g Vionate multivitamin powder, sprinkled on green food or ground meat.

Meat: 5 g finely ground.

Trogoniformes

TROGONS (QUETZALS)

The thirty-five species of trogons in the family Trogonidae are brightly coloured tropical birds with no close relatives. They are quiet, solitary inhabitants of tropical rain forests around the world. Most plentiful in the New World where twenty species occur, they are found from southern Arizona, Texas and the West Indies south through the equatorial belt to northern Argentina. Eleven species live in the Orient from India east to the Philippine Islands and south to Sumatra and Java. Three are found in the rich jungles of Africa. This is a wide range for such a small group of birds. Trogons are non-migratory and live in rather small territories where abundant fruits, berries and insects are available all year round.

The New World trogons live almost exclusively on fruits and berries, although a few insects are also eaten. In the Old World, the trogons feed extensively on insects, which they catch in flight. The Oriental and African forms forage for food like flycatchers, watching from a perch for their prey to fly by or crawl along a leaf. Then they dart out, capture the insects and return to the perch to swallow them. Because the Old World trogons are insectivorous, very few are imported as they are almost impossible to care for successfully in captivity.

The New World trogons, being fruit and berry eaters, are quite easily kept in aviaries and live for twelve to fourteen years with good husbandry.

Trogons are hole nesters and many lay their eggs in natural cavities in trees and stumps. Two to four rounded, white-greenish-blue eggs are laid. Incubation varies from sixteen to twenty-three days. Both sexes incubate, brood and rear the young.

In size, they vary from 23 to 96 cm in length. The legs and feet are small and weak in most species. The bill is short and wide. In the New World forms the bill is serrated for cutting the fruits and berries. The skin is thin and very tender. The body plumage is metallic with beautiful greens, blacks, reds, yellows and blues in pleasing patterns. Yoke-toes, two toes in front and two behind is characteristic of this and of similar arboreal groups such as the toucans, cuckoos, parrots and woodpeckers.

The Resplendent Trogon or Quetzal (*Pharomachrus mocino*) is the finest of all the trogons and has often been called the most beautiful bird in the world. Worshipped as the God of the Air by the ancient Aztecs and Mayas, the Quetzal has played an important part in their history and mythology. Today, this bird is the national bird of Guatemala and no specimen can be exported legally from that country. Quetzals range from southern Mexico to Costa Rica. With the destruction of its habitat, especially the cloud forest, the Quetzal has been placed on the list of endangered species and is strictly protected.

The Quetzal, 35.5 cm in length, plus its 61-cm tail, is metallic green in colour, with the breast and abdomen vermilion. The feathers of the head are lengthened to form a handsome crest and the greater wing coverts appear as living ferns, 61 cm in length, moving gently in the breeze. The bill is yellow and the feet are red. The female with her brown head, emerald green body plumage, scarlet under tail coverts and barred tail feathers is also very attractive.

Daily Diet for Trogons

Choice of fruit: 14 g papaya, grapes (cut in half), raisins (soaked overnight in water), avocados, figs or apples diced in small pieces.
Choice of berries: 14 g blueberries, blackberries or raspberries.
Cooked rice: 5 g.
Grated carrots: 5 g.
Insects: 2 g mealworms or pupae of mealworms.
Hard-boiled egg: 5 g, crumbled on top of cooked rice.
Minerals: 5 g Vionate multivitamin powder mixed with cooked rice.

Coraciiformes

HORNBILLS · ROLLERS · HOOPOES · MOTMOTS
BEE–EATERS · TODIES · KINGFISHERS

Hornbills

The family Bucerotidae contains forty-five species of hornbills, widely distributed throughout the tropical and subtropical forests of the Old World. When first seen, hornbills attract a great deal of attention. They are large in size, grotesque in appearance and most of them have strange nesting habits. In size they range from 38 to 152 cm in length. This group of birds will not live well without adequate protection in cold climates and should be housed in warm shelters during the winter months.

Trademarks of the hornbill family are the bill and casque which, according to the species, may be large or small, curved or straight, smooth or serrated. The ornamental casques or helmets cover the head and the base of the bill in many species. In some of the small species they are only indicated by a compressed ridge. Although hard and firm, they are not as heavy as they appear, being cellular bony structures inside. Each bill and casque is colourful, patterned in white, ivory, black, brown, red or yellow. Nature's purpose in providing such a bill is still a mystery. It has been suggested that, because of its strength and weight, it is used to excavate and to enlarge holes in trees and banks for nesting cavities. Again, the bill serves as a mason's trowel for applying plaster to the nesting hole.

Following the selection of a hollow tree and nesting hole, the male will partially seal the entrance of the hole with mud to imprison the female. During the incubation and brooding periods, he will feed his mate through a slit opening. Only the terrestrial Ground Hornbills of Africa do not practise this behaviour. The Ground Hornbills dig holes in burrows in clay banks or nest in open stumps of fallen trees. They do not imprison the females in their nests.

The distribution of the feather tracts is unusual in this family. In some, the spinal feather tract is not defined in the neck. In several of the larger species, the feathers are coarse, loose-webbed and wiry in shades of brown, black, white or typically black and white. Sexes are unlike in many species, alike in others. The tail consists of ten feathers, long and rounded.

The heavy bodies force the larger hornbills to exert tremendous energy during flight. The strong and powerful wings produce sounds resembling the noise of a steam engine when they beat in flight. All species have long spectacular hair-like eyelashes, providing eye protection. The bare skin about the eye is brightly coloured as is the bare throat in many species. In addition, several species are crested. The legs are short with the exception of the Ground Hornbill (*Bucorvus*). The feet are broad-soled and syndactyl (two or more toes joined for part of their length).

Hornbills are omnivorous (eating both plant and animal food). In captivity they will eat almost anything offered. They will accept budget-priced items such as bread and milk, boiled rice and kibbled dog food with Karo syrup. A basic diet of this type somewhat lessens the cost of satisfying their terrific appetites. The more costly fruits, berries, insects, rodents, frogs, snails, eggs and baby chicks may be fed as supplements.

They do make tame and affectionate pets, but most individuals need a strong cage or aviary to match the birds' size. They enjoy being petted and handled by adults and some will follow an owner about like a dog and command attention.

Daily Diet for: Concave Casqued (Great Pied) (*Buceros bicornis*); Bornean Rhinoceros (*Buceros rhinoceros borneoensis*); Wreathed (*Aceros undulatus*); Malabar Pied (*Anthracocerus coronatus*); Indian Pied (*Anthracocerus malabaricus*); Long-crested (Asiatic White-crested) (*Berenicornis comatus*); and Luzon Tarictic (*Penelopides panini manillae*) Hornbills

Ground meat: 14 g (fresh).

Vegetables: 5 g cooked sweet potatoes or diced carrots.

Boiled rice: 14 g.

Berries or fruits: 14 g choice of eugenia, mulberry, blackberry, straw-berries, pyracantha, banana, pear, apple, figs, grapes, raisins (soaked overnight in water), dates, tomatoes or ½ can fruit cocktail or diced fruits.

Rodents or chicks: 40 g field mice or coturnix quail chicks.

Egg: 28 g hard-boiled egg or fresh pigeon or quail eggs (2).

Snails: 12 g garden snails (2).

Vitamins: 2 g wheat germ oil mixed with ground meat.

Daily Diet for Red-billed Hornbill (*Tockus erythrorhynchus*)

Ground meat: 5 g.

Bread and milk: 5 g.

Berries and fruits: 14 g blueberries, mulberries, blackberries, apples, bananas, pears, grapes, figs, dates, cherries (all fruits diced), or strawberries.

Mice or rats: 20 g mice.

Egg: 14 g hard-boiled.

Insects: 5 g mealworms, fed twice daily.

Minerals: 5 g Vionate multivitamin powder sprinkled on meat.

Daily Diet for North African Ground Hornbill (*Bucorvus abyssinicus*)

Ground meat: 14 g.

Bread and milk: 14 g.

Berries or fruits: 14 g choice of blueberries, mulberries, blackberries, strawberries, apples, bananas, pears, grapes, figs, dates or cherries (fruit to be diced).

Rats: 400 g (1 rat, cut in three pieces).

Egg: 28 g hard-boiled.

Trout Chow pellets: 14 g.

Rollers

The eleven species of true Rollers (family Coraciidae) are pigeon-sized, 25 to 40 cm in length. This group of insectivorous birds inhabits the warmest regions of southern Africa, temperate Eurasia, Asia, Australia and eastward to the Pacific Islands. Rollers are masters in aerial acrobatics, displaying barrel-rolls, somersaults and tumbling when playing or in courtship.

Gaudy and stout, these brilliantly coloured birds wear shades of blue, green, turquoise, cinnamon, yellow, lilac and ultra-marine. The sexes are alike. The bill is broad and strong, the head large and the neck short. The wings and tail are long. They have short legs with weak feet. Rollers differ from other members of the Order in the foot structure. The two main toes are connected for much of their length, but the outer toes move freely.

They are solitary birds except during migration. Usually they are seen singly or in pairs. Noisy, pugnacious birds, they are normally seen perched on branches or wires. When flying insects, grasshoppers, locusts or flying ants pass, they dart out and capture their prey. Rollers also feed on small rodents, lizards and nestling birds when insects are absent.

Nests are made in holes or hollow trees, burrows, crevices in rocks and abandoned nests of other birds and mammals. Three to six white eggs are laid. Both sexes incubate the eggs, brood and care for the chicks.

In Australia, the Broad-billed Roller (Dollar Bird) (*Eurystomus orientalis*) does not nest every year, only in years when insects, usually locusts, are abundant. This bird takes its common name from the shining spot on its wings which resembles a silver dollar.

Hoopoes

The eye-catching Hoopoe has a family Upupidae all to itself. The nine races have an enormous range, being found in central and southern Eurasia, Asia, Malaysia, Africa and Madagascar. They are migratory, and have little fear of people. They are found in forest clearings, gardens, parks, orchards, and populated cities. They feed almost entirely on the ground, probing in the ground with their long bills for worms, larvae, grubs, ants and insects.

The delicate fawn colour, black-tipped erectile crest and the broad black and white wing and tail bands that show conspicuously in flight make these birds unmistakable. They are often called 'zebra' birds in Africa, because of this pattern.

Hoopoes are pictured on the walls of ancient tombs and temples in Egypt and Greece. Medieval writers mention them in connection with magic and supernatural events. In the Old Testament, this bird was incorrectly referred to as the 'lapwing' in the King James version. King Solomon's Bird is another name much more fitting because of the regal and spectacular crest.

Hoopoes nest in tree cavities and crevices in walls and buildings. In captivity, they nest easily in wooden boxes. In China, the hoopoe is called the 'Coffinbird' because it nests in holes in exposed coffins. The nests are lined with bits of grass and feathers. In the literature, nests have been described as filthy and odoriferous. We have found this to be untrue in our experience in raising these birds. Three to four eggs are laid each season. The female alone incubates the eggs and broods the chicks. Both sexes feed the chicks when two and a half weeks old. The incubation period is eighteen days. As in the case of the hornbills, the female on the nest is fed by the male during the incubation period.

The six species of Wood Hoopoes, family Phoeniculidae, are quite different from the related European Hoopoe. They are found in the forests of Africa, south of the Sahara. They measure from 23 to 43 cm in length. They are slimmer birds with long tails, no crests and with scimitar-shaped sharp bills.

The plumage is dark with blue and green metallic colouration. Sexes are similar, with the female being smaller and sometimes browner. They seldom come to the ground, finding their insect food and small berries in the bark and on high branches of trees. They forage in trees like woodpeckers with their sharp curved toenails which enable them to creep along in the branches. They are noisy birds, travelling in small family groups through the dense forests. Four to six eggs are laid each season. The female alone incubates the eggs and both parents care for the young.

Daily Diet for Hoopoes and Wood Hoopoes

Trout Chow: 5 g, moistened with water.
Minced meat: 5 g.
Hard-boiled egg: 5 g, crumbled and placed on Trout Chow.
Mealworms: 5 g (10).
Larvae: 5 g larvae of Larder Beetles (*Dermestes lardarius*) (or any small beetle of the Dermistids).
Earthworms: 14 g in separate container in 120 g of soil.
Vitamins: 5 g Vionate multivitamin sprinkled on minced meat.
Wheat Germ Oil: 2 drops sprinkled on hard-boiled egg.
Berries: 5 g blueberries. (For Thailand Hoopoe, raisins soaked overnight in water may be substituted for blueberries. *Raisins may not be substituted in the case of Wood Hoopoes.*)

Motmots

Motmots are a small group of birds with green, blue, cinnamon and black on their loose-webbed plumage. These forest birds are found exclusively in the New World, ranging from Mexico south to northern Argentina, Paraguay, Brazil, Tobago and the Trinidad Islands.

There are eight species, ranging in size from 15 to 61 cm in length. The crow-like bill is strong and serrated on the edges, adapted for holding lizards, small rodents, snails and large insects or fruit. In most species

of motmots, the central tail feathers are longer than the others and terminate in racquet-shaped tips. Often called the barber-birds, several of the
motmots shave the webbing of their tail feathers while preening as the
barbs near the end of the tail feathers are thin and not strongly attached
to the shaft. The tail wags stiffly, resembling the pendulum of a clock.
The sexes are alike in colouration.

The smallest of the motmots, the Tody Motmot (*Hylomanes momotula*)
of the forests in southern Mexico and Colombia, does not have the rac-
quets at the end of the tail as seen in most other species. It is dull green
and reddish brown in colour.

Most species nest in burrows, 1.2 to 1.8 m long, which both sexes dig
with their bills and feet. Nests may also be made in holes in hollow trees.
Three to four white eggs are laid in the nest with a few sticks, feathers
and pieces of grass to cushion the eggs. Incubation takes from seventeen
to twenty days and the chicks are fledged in four or five weeks. Both sexes
incubate, brood and feed the nestlings.

Motmots breed well in captivity in large, well-planted aviaries when
there is abundant insectivorous food. Commercial insect traps have been
manufactured by several companies which would be ideal for installation
on the tops of aviaries to supply the necessary insects.

Daily Diet for Motmots

Minced meat: 14 g.
Mice: 40 g—fed twice daily.
Lizards: 15 g.
Hard-boiled egg: 28 g.
Choice of insects: 5 g mealworms, crickets, grasshoppers or sphinx
  moth, fed twice daily.
Snails: 12g, fed twice daily.
Vitamins: 5 g sprinkled on meat.

Bee-eaters

Among the most attractive of Old World birds are twenty-four species
of bee-eaters (family Meropidae). They are found in southern Eurasia,
southern China, the East Indies to the Solomon Islands and in Australia
and Africa. They inhabit forested and open country. Most birds are
migratory, following large populations of insects in warmer climates. Bee-
eaters are difficult to keep alive in aviaries because of the large quantities

of insectivorous food which must be provided daily. More than one hundred kinds of insects may be eaten daily, although more than one half of those chosen are members of the bee and wasp family. Without insect traps and cultures of locusts, grasshoppers, crickets, roaches and mealworms available, bee-eaters should not be kept.

In size, these birds range from 15 to 36 cm in length. Many are brilliantly coloured in different shades of greens and blues, with bold patches of red, yellow, blue, white and black in their plumage. The wings are large and pointed. The tail is long, usually with two elongated central tail feathers. The bill is slender, ridged and down-curved. The feet are small and weak. Sexes are similar in colour. Bee-eaters perch on exposed branches, wires and roofs where they wait for flying insect life to pass by. Wonderful fliers, they hawk their prey and catch it in flight. In Africa and Australia great flocks of bee-eaters follow the grass fires attentively, capturing the locusts and other insects disturbed by the burning vegetation.

Most bee-eaters nest in vertical banks or ground burrows a metre or so in length with a chamber at the end for the eggs. Two to seven white eggs are laid in one clutch. The incubation period is twenty-one to twenty-two days. Both sexes incubate the eggs, brood and feed the chicks. The young fledge in four to five weeks and are still cared for by the parent birds. All bee-eaters are single-brooded and if abundant food is not available, the chicks die quickly.

Todies

The five species of todies are tiny relatives of the kingfishers and motmots. This family, Todidae, is restricted entirely to the West Indies. Three of them live in Cuba, Puerto Rico and Jamaica and two in Hispaniola. Todies have peculiarly flattened bills with fine serrations along the edges. All have prominent facial bristles and slender legs and feet. They are colourful birds with green heads and backs, red throats and light underparts. There are patches of white, pink, blue or yellow on the vents and flanks.

Todies live in wooded or brushy hillsides or ravines, often near streams. They are non-migratory and make a loud, whirring sound when they fly. Completely insectivorous, they sit quietly like kingfishers, darting out from a branch and returning at once with their insect prey. In size, they range from 9 to 11 cm in length. They nest in bank burrows, using the bill to dig, as do the kingfishers. The tunnel leading to the breeding chamber is 30 to 60 cm in length and opens into the chamber itself which is from 12 to 16 cm in diameter. Two or three white eggs are laid in the dirt. Both sexes incubate and feed the chicks.

Todies are tame and unsuspicious and may be captured easily with a butterfly net. Since they are tiny, they have few enemies. In Haiti, the native children visit the tody nests and collect the eggs for eating.

Diet for Cuban Tody (*Todus multicolor*) and Jamaican Tody (*Todus todus*)

Mealworms: 2 g.
Crickets: 2 g.
Houseflies: 2 g.
Vitamins: 2 g sprinkled on insects before feeding.

Daily diet should be divided and fed six times daily.

Kingfishers

The Kingfisher family, Alcedinidae, consists of eighty-six species which are world-wide in distribution. The majority are found in the tropical regions of the Old World. Six species occur in the New World but only one, the Belted Kingfisher (*Ceryle alcyon*) is found north of Mexico. Eurasia, too, has only one species, the European Kingfisher (*Alcedo atthis*). In Africa some fifteen species are represented. The remaining sixty-nine range from central Asia south to Australia and eastward to the Pacific islands as far as Samoa. Despite their common name, the majority are not fish-eating birds but prey on insects, small rodents, lizards, small birds and crustaceans.

The smallest in the family, the Pygmy Kingfisher (*Chloroceryle aenea*), is found over a large area in Africa. The largest, the Giant Kingfisher or Kookaburra (*Dacelo gigas*) of Australia seems to adapt best of the family to life in captivity. It reproduces in captivity when furnished with proper facilities and good nutrition. Many kingfishers live for only short periods in aviaries, especially the fish-eating group of which the Belted Kingfisher is a good example. The forest kingfisher has a varied diet and so is easier to feed under captive conditions.

Kingfishers range from 13 to 46 cm in length. All are similar in appearance, with chunky bodies, short necks, large heads and short tails. Their bills are long, strong and usually pointed. The legs are short, the feet small and weak. In some forms the sexes are alike, but they are unlike in others.

The fishing kingfishers are always found near water. They nest in holes in river banks while the forest kingfishers seek out tree cavities or make nest holes in termite nests. The eggs, two to eight in number, are white and are incubated for eighteen to twenty-four days. Both sexes incubate the eggs and care for the young.

Most kingfishers are brightly coloured, mainly in greens and blues, with contrasting patches or spots of red, white and cinnamon. Others are spotted and barred with bright red or yellow bills. The plumage is iridescent and immaculate because of their daily bathing.

Daily Diet for Kookaburra (Giant Kingfisher) (*Dacelo gigas*)

Ground meat: 14 g.
Rats: 400 g (cut into 4 pieces).
Mice: 20 g (1 at 7.00 am and 1 at 5.00 pm).
Snails: 6 g garden or vine snails, fed twice daily.
Vitamins: 5 g Vionate multivitamin powder sprinkled on meat.
Tree frogs: 133 g.

Diet for Kookaburra Chicks (fed by parents)

2.5 g baby mice, fed 4 times daily for three weeks, with Vionate sprinkled on the baby mice.

Daily Diet for Pygmy Kingfisher (*Chloroceryle aenea*)

Insects: 5 g mealworms fed in small flat container *or* crickets fed in cricket box.
Beef heart: 5 g cut in worm-like strips and fed in small separate container.
Small minnows: live, fed in minnow pool three times daily.
Minerals: 2 g Vionate powder, sprinkled on strips of meat.

Daily Diet for: White-breasted Kingfisher (*Halcyon smyrnensis fusca*); Javan White-collared Kingfisher (*Halcyon chloris palmeri*); Bengal White-collared Kingfisher (*Halcyon chloris humii*); and Burmese Stork-billed Kingfisher (*Pelargopsis capensis burmanica*)

Fish: 40 g anchovies or sardines, fed twice daily.
Frogs: 133 g tree frog.

Lizards: 20 g alligator lizard.
Crabmeat: 14 g.
Snails: 6 g garden snail, fed twice daily.
Insects: 10 mealworms, 2 crickets, Green June Beetles or May Beetles larvae when available—fed twice daily.
Ground meat: 14 g.
Minerals: 5 g Vionate multivitamin powder, sprinkled on meat.

Piciformes

Barbets

Barbets are a large family, Capitonidae, with seventy-five species. They are small to medium-sized birds, 11.5 to 30.5 cm in length. They are chunky little birds with short necks, big heads, large bills and prominent hair-like bristles about the nostrils. The name barbet derives from the French word *barbu*, meaning 'bearded'. They are brightly coloured in rich greens with bold patterns of reds, yellows and blues.

Many have loud and strident voices, others have pleasing low whistles. The calls of several Old World forms are metallic and are the reason they are sometimes called coppersmiths, blacksmiths and tinkerbirds. One of the most popular is the Crimson-breasted Barbet (*Megalaima haemacephala*) of India, the 'coppersmith' of Kipling's Rikki Tikki Tavi, whose metallic voice spread the good news when Rikki killed the cobras Nag and Nagaina.

Barbets are at home in the lush growth of tropical forests. They are seldom seen on the ground. They feed on fruits, berries, buds, blossoms and insects found on the outer tree branches. Most young are fed exlusively on insect life. A few adults live entirely on insects, tree ants and termites.

This family is widely distributed. In the New World, they range from Costa Rica to Peru and Brazil. In Africa they are found south of the Sahara. In Asia they are found from India through Malaysia to the Philippines, Sumatra and Borneo. All are non-migratory.

The largest is the Great Himalayan Barbet (*Megalaima virens*), 30 cm in length. It is green and red in colour and lives at the 2440 m level in the Himalayas.

The Toucan Barbet (*Semnornis ramphastinus*) is found in Ecuador, Colombia and in the Andes. It uses its large, strong bill as a chisel to excavate nesting holes. These birds sing duets and answer one another antiphonally when separated or forming pairs.

Barbets nest in tree holes, in tree ferns, in stream banks or termite nests. Two to five glossy white eggs are laid. The incubation period varies from thirteen to nineteen days. Both sexes excavate the nesting hole, incubate the eggs, and brood and feed the chicks. The chicks fledge in four or five weeks and are able to leave the nest.

Many of the barbets live very well in captivity on a varied diet of fruits, berries, soft food and insects. Twelve years seems to be a normal life in well planted aviaries.

The following diet has been used successfully for keeping the following barbets in captivity: Crimson-breasted (*Megalaima haemacephala*); Fire-tufted (*Psilopogon pyrolophus*); Red and Yellow (*Trachyphonus erythrocephalus*); Double-toothed (*Lybius bidentatus*); Toucan (*Semnornis ramphastinus*); Great Himalayan (*Megalaima virens*) and Lineated (*Megalaima lineata*).

Daily Diet for Barbets

Berries and fruits: 14 g mixture of pyracantha, mulberries, black-berries, raspberries, blueberries or cranberries with diced apple, orange, banana, figs, grapes, cherries, pears or peaches *or* 14 g of canned diced fruits in corn syrup.

Vegetables: 14 g cooked turnips, sweet potatoes, or carrots.

Insects: 5 g mealworms, crickets or adults and larvae of beetles, Green June Beetles or May Beetles.

Egg: 28 g hard-boiled.

Meat: 14 g ground meat.

Rodent: 2 g 'Pinky' mouse.

Minerals: 5 g Vionate multivitamin powder sprinkled on meat.

Toucans

The forty-one species of Toucans in the family Ramphasticae live in the tropical rain forests and wooded foothills from southern Mexico to Argentina, Paraguay and Brazil. They are most numerous in the forests along the Amazon.

Their large, painted bills and long fringed tongues which extend the entire length of the beak make them the most easily recognized birds in the New World. Although they appear top-heavy, the bill is really light and transparent, consisting of numerous stiff cellular fibres which give it maximal strength with minimal weight. Since they are heavy of body and short of wing, toucans use the long bills to reach fruits and berries at the tips of branches which would not support their weight. These birds measure from 30 to 61 cm in length. The largest are the true toucans, those which are medium in size are the aracaris (mountain toucans) and the smallest are called toucanets.

The name for these birds comes from the word *tucano*, which is their name among the Tupi Indians of Brazil.

As with other bright-coloured birds of the forest, the toucans' brilliant green and black body plumage is ornamented with red, orange, white and blue in broken patterns. Thus they harmonize with their surroundings and are hard to see when sitting quietly. The wings are short, the tail is square or graduated. The legs and feet are stout and strong, yoke-toed. Two toes are directly forward and two backward, as in the woodpeckers.

Toucans move about the jungle in small flocks, following the berries and fruits as they ripen. Insects, small rodents, lizards and bird eggs may also be eaten. They are noisy when feeding, chattering and clacking their bills as they clean them of sticky fruits and berries.

Most toucans nest in tree cavities, either natural ones or in abandoned woodpecker holes which they may enlarge slightly. Some nests are found near ground level, others high in tall trees. Two to four glossy white eggs are laid in the nest cavity. The incubation period varies from seventeen to nineteen days. Both sexes incubate, brood and care for the chicks. The young hatch naked and are completely helpless.

The chicks have prominent heel pads at the upper end of the tarsus. These pads support the bird's weight while it is in the nest. The chick's bill is broad and flat, the lower bill projecting beyond the tip of the upper. The tongue completely fills the bill cavity. The young develop and several months elapse before the nestling is able to leave the nest fully feathered. The heel pads slough off before the chicks leave the nest.

In captivity these birds make excellent pets and live ten to twelve years with good care. They are easy to feed with fresh or canned fruits and berries supplemented with insects, eggs, bread and milk, vitamins and an occasional baby mouse.

In the last few years, several species have nested and successfully reared young. The Toco Toucan (*Ramphastos toco*), Red-breasted Toucan (*Ramphastos dicolorus*) and the Crimson-rumped Toucanet (*Aulacorhynchus haematopygus*) have nested in Florida, Texas and California. Others have reproduced in Eurasia.

Daily Diet for Toucans, Toucanets, Aracaris

Fruits and berries: 14g diced fresh fruit mixture of figs, bananas, apples, pears, cherries, grapes, raisins, currants (soaked overnight in water) or tomatoes; *or* 14 g canned diced fruit cocktail together with pyracantha, eugenia, blackberries, raspberries or mulberries.

Bread and milk: 14 g.

Egg: 28 g, hard-boiled, crumbled.

Insects: 5 g.

Mice: 2 g baby mouse.

ZuPreem Soft-bill Diet: 14 g.

Vitamins: 5 g Vionate multivitamin powder sprinkled on egg.

Woodpeckers

The family Picidae, woodpeckers, consists of 209 species living in woodlands of the tropic and temperate zones through the world. They are absent only in Australia, New Zealand, the Malagasy Republic, the polar regions and the oceanic islands.

They range in size from 9 to 56 cm in length. All are yoke-toed (zygodactyl), having the toes arranged two in front and two behind. They have pointed bills for chipping wood, heavily clawed toes for climbing tree trunks, stiffened tail feathers for bracing themselves on vertical surfaces and long sticky, barbed tongues for digging grubs and larvae out of holes and ants out of the ground or trees.

Fruits, berries and nuts are eaten by many when insectivorous food is absent. Flickers are ant-eating woodpeckers. Sapsuckers drill holes in trees and lick up the flowing sap. All types of insects and their larvae are eaten. Acorns are the favourite food of many woodpeckers and great numbers are collected and stored for winter food. Almonds are also enjoyed by a few species. The seeds of magnolia, bayberry, poison oak, poison ivy, pines and conifer trees are eaten. Orange, apricot, plum and apple orchards are sometimes visited, but not regularly.

The colours of woodpeckers are varied black and white, browns, greens, with red and yellow head markings. Some are streaked, barred and spotted. The Crimson-winged Woodpecker (*Picus puniceus*) of Malaysia has a beautiful crimson crest to match its wings.

Nests are made in holes of trees, cacti and cliff banks. The holes are chiselled out with the bill. The smaller species sometimes use old woodpecker holes. Two to eight white eggs are laid and both sexes share the incubation, brooding and care of the chicks. The incubation period varies from eight to sixteen days. Two broods may be raised each year.

The chicks are naked and blind when first hatched and are reared in the nest.

Woodpeckers are not easy subjects in captivity because of the specialized diets of ants and insects required by many species. Some of the larger species may be kept in spacious flight cages which have been provided with trees and branches on which they can climb and exercise. Dead trees with holes should be available for them to sleep. If no trees or branches are available in the aviary, woodpeckers will climb on the wire sides and soon destroy the tail feathers by abrasion from the wire surface.

They can be well nourished on chopped meat, hard-boiled eggs, sunflower seeds, hazelnuts, walnuts, peanuts, peanut butter, conifer seeds, vitamins and insects.

The following birds have been kept successfully on the diet presented below: Red-headed Woodpecker (*Melanerpes erythrocephalus*); Red-shafted Flicker (*Colaptes auratus cafer*); Lesser Golden-backed Woodpecker (*Dinopium benghalense*); Golden-fronted Woodpecker (*Melanerpes aurifrons*); Black-cheeked Woodpecker (*Melanerpes pucherani*); Green Woodpecker (*Picus viridis*); and White Woodpecker (*Leuconerpes candidus*).

Daily Diet for Woodpeckers

Beef suet: 5 g.

Nuts: 2 g, choice of peanuts, hazelnuts, almonds, walnuts or acorns.

Fruits: 5 g mixture of diced apples, prunes, apricots, or oranges with pyracantha, eugenia or bayberries.

Egg: 28 g hard-boiled.

Seeds: 14 g sunflower, conifer cones, pine seeds, maple, willow beech or aspen seeds.

Insects: 5 g mealworm, May Beetles, Green June Beetles, caterpillars, moths, crickets or grasshoppers.

Vitamins: 5 g Vionate multivitamin powder sprinkled on meat.

For a group of six to ten birds in quarantine, the following diet should be prepared for the daily requirements of the entire group.

Pablum Baby Food: 28 g. (Alternatives are: Oatmeal, Pinhead edible; Porridge Oats edible; Egg Biscuit Food. All available from John E. Haith, Park Street, Cleethorpes, South Humberside.)

Calcium Lactate: 1 g.

Trout Chow: 14 g.

Ground dried beef heart: 5 g.

Ground hemp seed: 1 g.
Wheat germ oil: 1 g.
Ground carrots: 9 g.
Crumbled hard-boiled egg: 9 g.

Mix all ingredients thoroughly and add enough water to make mixture crumbly but not soft. Feed in shallow dish.

Passeriformes

BIRDS OF PARADISE · BOWERBIRDS · PITTAS ·
COTINGAS · BROADBILLS · CROWS · APOSTLEBIRDS ·
MANAKINS · BULBULS · THRUSHES · MOCKINGBIRDS ·
ORIOLES · TANAGERS · LARKS · HONEYCREEPERS ·
LEAFBIRDS · WAGTAILS · STARLINGS · SUNBIRDS ·
WHITE-EYES · WARBLERS · FINCHES

Birds of Paradise

New Guinea and the adjacent islands are the home of the Birds of Paradise. A few species have drifted into northern Australia and the Louccas. Forty species have been well described in the family Paradisaeidae. All are forest birds, many living high in the mountains, wandering singly or in pairs except when feeding on a fruit tree or when displaying in a communal tree.

These ornate and colourful birds have dazzled the eye of man since before the sixteenth century. Males wear elaborate plumes, wires, tabs, capes, gorgettes and shields of pure and iridescent colours which they display in the breeding season. In some species, even the lining of the mouth is coloured to aid in the display.

The smallest is the size of a warbler, 14 cm. The King Bird of Paradise (*Cicinnurus reginus*) is one of the most brilliant; bright scarlet above and white below. The largest is the Brown (Long-tailed) Sicklebill Bird of Paradise (*Epimachus meyeri*), 101 cm in length. It is the size of a crow and is seldom found below an elevation of 1520 m.

Fruits and berries are their commonest food, but they also take insects, tree-frogs and small lizards. Information about nests is known for only a few species. Those which have reproduced in captivity made nests in clumps of bamboo, low shrubs. Some used open-topped boxes with twigs, leaves and feathers for lining the nest. The little King Birds of Paradise nested in a parakeet box in Sweden.

Two eggs are usually laid, white and heavily streaked with a brownish-lavender pattern. The incubation period varies from seventeen to twenty-two days. The female alone builds the nest, incubates the eggs and broods and cares for the chicks. Even in well-planted aviaries, the male must be separated from the female as soon as the nest is completed as the male will break the eggs and kill the chicks if left in the same aviary. Since they are endangered species, birds of paradise which are now in captivity must be carefully tended and nurtured.

Daily Diet for: Brown (Long-tailed) Sicklebill (*Epimachus meyeri*); Ribbon-tailed Bird of Paradise (*Astrapia mayeri*); Princess Stephanie's Bird of Paradise (*Astrapia stephaniae*); Lesser Bird of Paradise (*Paradisaea minor*); Count Raggi's Bird of Paradise (*Paradisaea apoda raggiana*); Prince Rudolph's Blue Bird of Paradise (*Paradisaea rudolphi*); Lesser Superb Bird of Paradise (*Lophorina superba*); Magnificent Bird of Paradise (*Diphyllodes magnificus*); and King Bird of Paradise (*Cicinnurus regius*)

Fruit: 7g mixture of papaya, grapes, figs, apple, bananas, raisins (soaked overnight in water) or ½ can diced fruit *fed in the morning*.

Berries: 7g eugenia, pyracantha, blueberries, mulberries or blackberries *fed in the evening*.

Hard-boiled egg: 28g crumbled.

Cooked rice: 5g.

Vegetables: 5g fresh grated carrots, shredded lettuce.

Insects: 5g mealworms (5–6) or earthworms (12 fed in leafmould feeding box).

Rodents: 1 'pinky' mouse or ½ small mouse fed every other day.

Trout Chow: 5g mixed with cooked rice.

Minerals: 5g Vionate multivitamin powder sprinkled on rice.

Note: papaya is the favourite food of birds of paradise.

Bowerbirds

There are seventeen species of bowerbirds found in Australia and New Guinea. Their name comes from the stick bowers built by the males used in displaying for the females. The catbirds of New Guinea are included in this family although they do not build bowers.

In size, these birds range from 23 to 38 cm in length. They are largely solitary and terrestrial. They feed on the ground and in trees on fruits, berries, seeds, insects and small invertebrates. The bowers are used only for courtship displays.

Nests are loose open cups of leaves, twigs and feathers made in trees or vines constructed by the females alone. One to three white eggs with brown streaking are laid. The female incubates the eggs alone, broods the chicks and both sexes feed the chicks. The life history of these birds is little known. Nesting occurs only when abundant insect life is available.

The males of most species are colourful with much green, red, violet, yellow and orange in the plumage. The females are usually plainly coloured with camouflaged colours. Sexes are alike in a few species. Some have crests but none have the fantastic plumes of the birds of paradise.

Bowerbirds have developed skills as architects and decorators found in no other family of birds. The bowers are decorated with fern fronds, colourful beetle wings, snail shells and pieces of resin and berries to attract the females to the playground and courtship arenas.

In aviaries and large flight cages bowerbirds and catbirds are secretive and aloof. Rain forest aviaries provide ideal habitats for this group. Insect traps on the top of aviaries would provide the insectivorous food which is required daily.

The Regent (*Sericulus chrysocephalus*), Satin (*Ptilonorhynchus violaceus*), Spotted (*Chlamydera maculata*) and Fawn-breasted (*Chlamydera cerviniventris*) Bowerbirds and the Green (*Ailuroedus crassirostris*) and White-eared (*Ailuroedus buccoides*) Catbirds have been kept successfully on the following diet.

Daily Diet for Bowerbirds and Catbirds

Minced meat: 5 g.

Fruits and berries: Mixture of diced banana, apple, figs, grapes, raisins (soaked overnight in water), guavas, eugenia, pyracantha, mulberry or blackberry *or* ½ can diced fruit cocktail.

Insects and rodents: ½ mouse (10 g) plus mealworms, crickets, May Beetles, Green June Beetles, sphinx moths or grasshoppers for a total of 14 g.

Snails: 6 g.

Vegetables: 5 g grated carrots, shredded lettuce.

Hard-boiled egg: 28 g crumbled on meat.

Trout Chow: 5 g mixed with minced meat.

Minerals: 5 g Vionate multivitamin powder sprinkled on meat.

Pittas

Pittas, or 'jewel thrushes', are small and often brilliantly coloured ground birds that inhabit dense tropical forests in the Old World. They range through Indo–Malaysia to Australia and Africa.

The twenty-three species in the family Pittidae are plump birds with stubby tails and long legs. The bill is strong and slightly down–curved. The wings are short and rounded. They are poor fliers, hopping on the ground to feed on insects, worms and snails. At night they roost in low trees.

All are extremely beautiful with bold patches of greens, purple, reds and yellows. In many countries they are called Painted Thrushes. They measure from 16 to 28 cm in length.

Secretive birds, pittas are not easy to manage in captivity and are difficult to observe, even with their vivid colouration.

Nests are made in wet tropical forests in the thickest cover of ferns, vines and thorny bushes. The nest is globular in shape with a side entrance, constructed of twigs and vegetable fibres. The eggs number four to six and are glossy white with flecks of dark brown. In shape they are round like owl eggs. Both parents incubate and care for the young. The incubation period varies from seventeen to nineteen days.

Pittas live well in captivity in green-houses and arboretums. The best floor covering is deep peat moss or leaf mould which should be kept moist at all times. In aviaries the roof should be completely covered and natural branches should be provided for roosts. A semi-rotten log on the floor is always enjoyed. In the winter months pittas must be kept in warm houses. Dry sand should never be placed on the floor in quarantine stations. Astro–turf or rubber moulding will prevent injury to the pittas' feet.

Daily Diet for Pittas

Insects: 14 g mealworms and beetles, crickets, May Beetles, Green June Beetles or sphinx moths.
Worms: 14 g earthworms fed in leaf-mould feeding box.
Ground meat: 5 g.
ZuPreem Soft-billed bird diet: 5 g.
Berries: 5 g blueberries.
Snails: 6 g garden or vine snails.
Minerals: 5 g Vionate multivitamin powder sprinkled on ground meat.

Note: Feed half at 7 am and half at 5 pm.

Cotingas

The Cotinga family, Cotingidae, has seventy-one species. It is found in the tropics and subtropics and contains many brilliantly coloured birds. They range from southern Arizona and Texas southward to southern Brazil, northern Argentina and Bolivia, but are not found in Chile. Cotingas are most abundant in thick forest, rarely ascending the mountains as high as the subtropic zones. They feed on fruit and insects and are rather solitary in their habits.

In size, they vary from the tiny Kinglet Calyptura (*Calyptura cristata*) of eastern Brazil which is 8 cm in length to the giant Amazonian Umbrella Bird (*Cephalopterus ornatus*) which is 48 cm in length, found in the Guianas, Venezuela, Colombia, Peru, Bolivia and Brazil. A single species lives in Jamaica.

Some species show enamel-like blue and purple colours and others are grey and black. Still others are bright orange, yellow, crimson, green, snow-white or wine red. Some possess crests and wattles and others have bare heads and necks. All are noisy birds with very loud voices. Some voices are metallic and bell-like, others emit whistling, grunting and rumbling sounds.

Some nests are made in tree cavities, others are open nests in vines and ferns or on branches and domed over the top with grasses, twigs and leaves. Mud nests are also made on rock walls near waterways. One to six eggs with brownish spots are laid and the female alone incubates the eggs. The male guards the nest and both parents feed and care for the chicks. The incubation period in the genus Piprelo is eighteen or nineteen days.

The Orange (Guianan) Cock of the Rock (*Rupicola rupicola*) of northeastern South America is characterized by orange plumage in the male and brown in the female, a half-moon crest and ornamental wavy feathers on the back. The larger Scarlet Cock of the Rock (*Rupicola peruviana*) of western Colombia is red and grey and its crest is thick and full. The Bare-throated Bellbird (*Procnias nudicollis*) is snowy-white and lives in south-eastern Brazil. Its voice resembles a clear ringing bell and attracts attention whenever it is heard. Most outstanding of the Cotingas is the Long-wattled Umbrella Bird (*Cephalopterus penduliger*) with its neck wattle up to 46 cm in length. Both sexes are black, glossed with blue. They are found in Colombia and western Ecuador.

Daily Diet for: Orange (Guianan) Cock of the Rock (*Rupicola rupi-cola*); Scarlet Cock of the Rock (*Rupicola peruviana*); Bare-throated Bellbird (*Procnias nudicollis*) and Long-wattled Umbrella Bird (*Cephalopterus penduliger*)

Fruit: 28 g—mixture of diced orange, apple, banana and papaya *or* ½ can fruit cocktail or diced fruit.
Berries: 5 g eugenia, pyracantha or blackberries.
Insects: 5 g crickets or mealworms (4–5).
Trout Chow: 5 g moistened and mixed with hard-boiled egg.
Egg: 28g crumbled.
Minerals: 5 g Vionate multivitamin powder sprinkled on fruit.

The above diet is used for the Black-throated (Green and Black) Fruit-eater (*Pipreola riefferii*) and the Orange-breasted Fruit-eater (Cotinga) (*Pipreola jucunda*) with the addition of blueberries or currants which have been soaked overnight, and three or four minnows.

Broadbills

The fourteen species of broadbills in the family Eurylaimidae are a small group. They are vivid in colours, noisy and tame in gardens and fields. All live in the Old World, ranging from Africa to the Philippines. They are forest birds, liking cut-over secondary forests, wet jungles and mangrove swamps.

In size they vary from 13 to 28 cm in length. They are chunky with large heads and wide, flat, heavy hooked bills. Some have beautiful crests. The plumage is soft, silky green and blue in the Asian species. In the African forms the colours are more sombre with patches of yellow, lavender and red.

Broadbills' calls are varied, with froglike croaks, trilling, metallic whir-ring sounds and klaxon horn notes.

We had the opportunity of collecting specimens of the Lesser Green Broadbill (*Calyptomena viridis*) in Borneo. Broadbills make very attractive nests which are waterproof. They weave a long hanging purse-like structure of grasses, rootlets and other fibres, tapered both at the top and bottom. This they suspend by a single piece of vine or fibre. The centre of the nest where the eggs are laid is entered through a hole in the side, similar to a weaver's nest. Three to five buff eggs are laid, which have spots at the larger end. Both sexes build the nest, incubate the eggs and care for the young. The length of incubation is still unknown in many species.

Daily Diet for: Black and Red (*Cymbirhynchus macrorhynchus*); Lesser Green (*Calyptomena viridis*); African (Delacour's) (*Smithornis capensis*); Dusky (*Corydon sumatranus*) and Long-tailed (*Psarisomus dalhousiae*) Broadbills

Fruits: 14 g mixture of diced apples, pears, figs, grapes, raisins (soaked overnight in water) *or* ½ can diced fruit.
Berries: 14 g blueberries.
Insects: 5 g crickets, mealworms, May Beetles, Green June Beetles, moths or grubs.
Trout Chow: 5 g mixed with blueberries.
Baby mice: 2 g 'pinky' mouse.
Minerals: 5 g Vionate or any multivitamin powder sprinkled on fruit and berries.

Crows, Jays and Magpies

Crows, jays and magpies number 102 species and are almost cosmopolitan in distribution. They are absent in Antarctica and some oceanic islands. Living in varied habitats, most prefer woodlands and open brush lands. The majority are non-migratory.

They range from 20 to 71 cm in length. The American Raven (*Corvus corax*) is the largest-bodied bird in this family. One characteristic shared by the entire family, Corvidae, is their boldness and aggressiveness.

Some members are all black in colour. Others such as the crows, ravens and jackdaws are black and grey. The magpies wear dress coats of black and white with long tails. The smaller jays are often brightly coloured with patterns of blues, greens, yellows, pink and brown.

All feed on both animal and vegetable substances. No other group has such a varied diet. Crows are notorious for raiding row crops and eating fresh corn in the fields. They will eat almost anything, carrion, nuts, fish, shellfish, and the remains of small mammals killed on highways. Magpies feed on small birds and eggs and some have raided poultry farms in search of chicken eggs. Jays are aggressive too, stealing untended picnic lunches in sacks and boxes.

[139]

Most are beneficial, destroying many agricultural pests and insects. Insecticides continue to destroy much of their natural food but all are opportunists and most are able to face any disaster or emergency because of their intelligence and cunning.

Crows and ravens build simple stick nests. Magpies have bulky massive nests and jays have open cup nests in trees and on cliffs. The grey-necked jackdaws in Eurasia nest in holes in stone buildings. All are prolific with three to ten eggs laid each breeding season. Some eggs are white, others are greenish and speckled. The female incubates the eggs alone. Incubation periods vary from sixteen to twenty-five days. Both parents feed and care for the chicks.

Pairs of birds should be housed in individual aviaries for propagation and breeding. Again, insectivorous food must be used when nestlings hatch, as commercial mixed food will be ignored and the chicks will be thrown out of the nest if natural food is not provided for the parent birds.

Adult birds are easy to feed in captivity. Crows and ravens may live for twenty to twenty-five years with normal care. Jays usually live twelve to fifteen years in collections. Magpies are long-lived, too, reaching ages of fifteen to twenty years in well-planted aviaries.

Daily Diet for: Common Crow (*Corvus brachyrhynchos*); Fish Crow (*Corvus ossifragus*); American Raven (*Corvus corax*); White-necked Raven (*Corvus cryptoleucus*); Black-billed (Common) Magpie (*Pica pica*); Yellow-billed Magpie (*Pica nuttalli*); Clark's Nutcracker (*Nucifraga columbiana*) and the Black-backed Magpie (*Gymnorhina tibicen*)

Ground meat: 411 g.
Fruit: 75 g apple, orange and pears cut in half.
Nuts: 14 g acorns, almonds, peanuts and pine nuts (2 to 3).
Fish: 40 g smelt (for the Fish Crow).
Rodents: 40 g.
Chicks: 51 g.
Fresh eggs: 57 g raw egg, crumbled with shell on meat.
Choice of insects: 14 g grasshopper, locusts, crickets, beetles, grubs, moths or mealworms.
Trout Chow: 5 g mixed with meat.
Minerals: 5 g Vionate or any multivitamin powder sprinkled on meat.

The Hawaiian Crow (*Corvus tropicus*) should be given the same diet, with the addition of cactus fruit, papaya and ohia berries to the fruit.

Daily Diet for: Blue Jay (*Cyanocitta cristata*); **Steller's Jay** (*Cyanocitta stelleri*); **Scrub Jay** (*Aphelocoma coerulescens*); **Canada (Grey) Jay** (*Perisoreus canadensis*); **Green Jay** (*Cyanocorax yncas*); **European (Eurasian) Jay** (*Garrulus glandarius*); **Loo-choo (Lidth's) Jay** (*Garrulus lidthi*); **Pileated (Plush-crested) Jay** (*Cyanocorax chrysops*) **and Hunting Cissa (Green Magpie)** (*Cissa chinensis*)

Ground meat: 14 g.

Fruit and berries: 28 g apples, oranges, pears and papayas cut in halves plus 5–6 eugenia, pyracantha, blackberries, cranberries or blueberries *or* canned fruit cocktail or diced fruit.

Seeds or nuts: 14 g sunflower seeds, peanuts, almonds, acorns or pine nuts.

Cottage cheese: 15 g.

Rodents: 10 g 'pinky' mice or pieces of small mouse, given three times weekly.

Insects: 5 g crickets, mealworms, beetles, grasshoppers, moths or grubs.

Hard-boiled egg: 28 g crumbled on meat.

Trout Chow: 5 g mixed with meat.

Minerals: 5 g Vionate or any multivitamin powder sprinkled on meat.

Apostlebirds

The Apostlebirds (*Struthidea cinerea*) of Australia get their name from the habit of travelling in flocks of twelve. They are grey birds about 30 cm in length which live in dry country, feeding on insects and seeds. They nest in a mud nest plastered on a horizontal branch high in a tree. The Australian Magpie Lark (*Grallina cyanoleuca*) is another mud-nest builder. It is black and white and is found all over the countryside feeding on insects, earthworms and snails. Somewhat smaller than the Apostlebirds, it measures 28 cm in length.

A normal nest is made of mud 15 cm in diameter, with walls 2 cm thick. Three or four eggs are laid. They are white, marked with brown and black. The incubation period of Apostlebirds is twenty to twenty-one days. Magpie Larks incubate their eggs thirteen to fourteen days. Incubation, brooding and feeding of chicks is shared by both sexes in the mud-nest builders.

Daily Diet for Apostlebird, Magpie Lark

Minced meat: 5 g.
Egg: 28 g hard-boiled, crumbled and mixed with cottage cheese.
Cottage cheese: 5 g.
Insects: 14 g mealworms or crickets, grasshoppers (2–3).
Seeds: 5 g.
Trout Chow: 5 g.
Minerals: 5 g Vionate multivitamin powder sprinkled on meat.

Manakins

Manakins, of the family Pipridae, are found only in tropical America from Mexico to Argentina. They are non-migratory and there are fifty-nine species in the family. The largest populations are centred in Brazil, Venezuela and the Guianas.

All are small stocky birds the size of sparrows, ranging from 9 to 15 cm in length. Most have short wings and tails and a short bill. Thick primary forests and woodlands are their homes.

They perform curious displays and dances in communal areas. This is accompanied by popping and snapping noises, produced by their unusual modified wing feathers. They are often as spectacular in their own way as the displays of the much larger birds of paradise.

Most of the males are black, with brilliant patches of red, yellow, blue and orange on the head, back or thighs. The females are all olive-green or plainly coloured little birds and the species are difficult to tell apart.

Manakins live on small berries and insects and sometimes may be seen in the mixed flocks of antbirds, tanagers and other insect-eaters as they follow swarms of flying insects in the dense jungle. They move about singly or in small bands except during the breeding season, when males congregate on their 'dancing grounds' to form their harems.

Each female builds her own nest, incubates the two spotted eggs and rears the young by herself. The incubation period is nineteen to twenty days. The chicks fledge in two to three weeks, but do not develop the brilliant colour patches and plumage until two years of age.

Nests are frail little baskets of grasses and fibres woven and fastened between the forks of a horizontal branch.

Manakins are very easily kept. They are long-lived good aviary birds when fed properly. Their favourite food is fresh or canned blueberries.

Currants and raisins, soaked overnight in water until soft, are also well liked. When they are eating well, diced apple, pear, cherries, oranges, bananas, papaya, grapes and finely grated carrots may be offered. Minced meat may be mixed with the diced fruits.

The container of diced fruits should be hung on the wire side of the cage or fastened and hung on a branch in a low tree. Manakins do not like to feed on the ground or floor. Sprays or clusters of eugenia and pyracantha berries may also be hung in the aviary on shrubs or on the wire sides.

White-bearded (*Manacus manacus*), Long-tailed (*Chiroxiphia linearis*), Round-tailed (*Pipra chlormeros*), Yellow-thighed (Red-capped) (*Pipra mentalis*) and Pearl headed (Opal-crowned) (*Pipra iris*) Manakins have been kept successfully, using the following diet.

Daily Diet for Manakins

Berries or fruits: 5 g blueberries, eugenia, pyracantha, diced apple, orange, pear, banana, papaya, cherries or currants or raisins soaked overnight in water.

Minced meat: 5 g.

Trout Chow: 5 g moistened with water poured off, then mixed with diced fruit.

Grated carrots: 5 g.

Minerals: 5 g Vionate or any multivitamin powder sprinkled on blueberries or diced fruit.

Bulbuls

Bulbuls are familiar garden birds in the Old World tropics. They are widely distributed in Africa and in Asia to Japan, the Philippines, Moluccas and Borneo. One hundred and nineteen species have been well described in the family Pychonotidae. They range in size from 15 to 28 cm in length. A few are sparrow-sized but most of them are the size of blackbirds and many are enjoyed as excellent song birds.

Most bulbuls are olive-green, grey or brown with bright patches of red, yellow or white on the face and under the tail. Several are crested and the sexes are alike in colouration.

They live in mountain forests, lowland gardens and city parks, feeding on fruit, berries, buds, nectar and insects. A few have been restricted from importation into the Western Hemisphere in order to prevent damage to ripening crops. Bulbuls were introduced and released in Hawaii and have been proved to be quite beneficial, eating more insects than fruit wherever they are found.

Bulbuls build strong, open cup-shaped nests woven of hair, grasses, moss, bark and leaves. The nests are often lined with pine needles, rootlets and the slender leaves of bamboo. They are usually well concealed and difficult to find. They are placed at heights of 2.5 to 6 m in a tree or bamboo thicket. Two to four beautiful eggs, pinkish-grey in colour, with reddish-brown spots or purple blotches, are laid. Incubation takes twelve to fifteen days. Both sexes share the incubation of the eggs, brooding and care of the chicks. The nestlings' eyes open when five days old. Live insect food is fed for the first two weeks. Minced meat and small berries are fed to the young birds later, in addition to insectivorous food.

All bulbuls live well in confinement in well-planted aviaries or flight cages. They are active, sociable birds with clear ringing notes and are easy to care for, even for beginning aviculturists.

Daily Diet for Bulbuls

Choice of fruits: 14 g oranges, apples, bananas, papaya ($\frac{1}{4}$), raisins soaked overnight in water *or* $\frac{1}{4}$ can diced fruit or fruit cocktail.

Choice of berries: 5 g blueberries, elderberries, eugenia, pyracantha, or cotoneaster.

Choice of insects: 5 g crickets, mealworms, beetles, May Beetles, Green June Beetles or moths.

Trout Chow: 5 g mixed with minced meat.

Minced meat: 5 g.

Egg: 28 g hard-boiled.

Minerals: 5 g Vionate or any multivitamin powder sprinkled on meat.

Thrushes

There are 306 species of thrushes in the family Turdidae, and they are some of the finest songbirds in the world. No other family has so many members famed for their music—the European Nightingale, the Song Thrush, the Shama Thrush, the European Blackbird, the Blue Solitaire, the Hermit Thrush and the Wood Thrush, to name but a few.

Though essentially insectivorous, thrushes do not catch insects in flight. They feed on the ground as well as in trees and shrubs. They eat more fruit and berries than flycatchers and warblers do. Snails and slugs are eaten by some forms. Worms, seeds and leaves may also be eaten.

They are strong fliers and extremely adaptable. Few areas of the world except the Arctic are without some members of this family. Most thrushes are ground birds, their habitat varying from semi-desert to tropical rain-forests and from treeless plain regions to gardens, lawns and parks.

They are medium-sized birds, ranging in size from 11 to 33 cm in length. All have slender bills, large eyes, stout legs and feet. Wings are rounded or pointed. Browns, greys and blues are the common colours, with bold patterns of red, black and white blended in. Sexes may be alike or unlike. Immature thrushes are usually spotted on the under-parts. Although they are usually solitary birds, many travel in flocks during migration and the winter months.

Nests are constructed in both trees and shrubs or on the ground. Rock cavities or tree holes may also be used. The open cup-shaped nests are made of grasses, rootlets, fibres or sticks and are often lined with mud. Four blue-green eggs are laid by the American Robin (*Turdus migratorius*). The incubation period is fourteen days and the chicks fledge in two to three weeks. The female incubates the eggs alone and also broods the chicks. Both parents feed and care for the nestlings.

Thrushes of many species may be kept safely together with tanagers, honeycreepers, larks and wagtails in large flight cages and aviaries as their diets are so similar.

The use of one of the blacklite safety insect traps should be useful in providing the large quantities of insectivorous food needed for this family. Earthworms, crickets and mealworms are readily available from commercial suppliers in many countries. They are advertised in avicultural bulletins and periodicals.

Daily Diet for: American Robin (*Turdus migratorius*); **Wood Thrush** (*Hylocichla mustelina*); **Eastern Bluebird** (*Sialia sialis*); **Shama Thrush** (*Copsychus malabaricus*); **Nightingale** (*Luscinia megarhynchos*); **Eurasian Robin** (*Erithacus rubecula*); **Orange-headed Ground Thrush** (*Zoothera citrina*); **Blue (Slate-coloured) Solitaire** (*Myadestes unicolor*); **Snowy-headed Robin-chat** (*Cossypha niveicapilla*); **and Blue Whistling Thrush** (*Myiophoneus caeruleus*)

Earthworms and insects: 14 g—earthworms (fed in garden soil in separate box), mealworms and beetles (8 to 10), flies, crickets, moths, butterfly moths, spiders, May Beetles, Green June Beetles, grubs, snails (1–2).

Fruits and berries: 5 g diced apples, pears, cherries, grapes, currants or raisins soaked overnight in water, blueberries, pyracantha, cotoneaster or mulberries.

Hard-boiled egg: 28 g mixed with pound cake and Trout Chow.

Pound cake: 5 g crumbled and mixed with Trout Chow.

Trout Chow: 5 g mixed with egg.

Minerals: 5 g Vionate or any multivitamin powder sprinkled on egg mixture.

Mockingbirds

The Mockingbird (*Mimus polyglottos*) is 27 cm in length. It is a member of the Mimine Thrush family, Mimidae, which is a small family of thirty-one species, including mockingbirds, thrashers and catbirds. Exclusively American, it is distributed from Canada to southern Argentina and Chile

Mockingbird menu

Preferred Foods	Second Choice	Will Not Eat
apple	blackberries	peanut butter
corn	apricot	cottage cheese
tomato seeds	pomegranate	butter
avocado	grapes	suet
sauerkraut	apple sauce	dog food
white bread	pokeberries	bananas
papaya	pear	dogwood berries
mealworms	rice (cooked)	white potato
grasshoppers	milk	corn bread
spiders	strawberries	sweet potato
ants	lettuce	persimmon
ant eggs	chickweed	plum
moths	carrot tops (sprouted)	any citrus fruits
caterpillars	parsley	cranberries
	liver fat	sugar
	soaked raisins	buttermilk
	peach	molasses
	hard-boiled egg	cherries
	ground egg shell (sterilized)	

2 drops of cod liver oil and 2 drops wheat germ oil on small piece of bread every day. Otherwise, diet is varied as the mockingbird seems to prefer a daily change.

and from the West Indies to the Galapagos Islands. The habitat is brushland, forest edges, hedgerows and shrubbery. It feeds on the ground and in shrubs on a diet of insects, fruits, berries and seeds. Most are slender with long legs and tails. They are grey, slate or brown with paler underparts, which are often white, streaked or spotted.

The mockingbird which lives in the southern part of the USA is a master at imitating the songs of other birds. As many as thirty other bird songs have been imitated. It can also imitate the sounds of hens or frogs.

Nests are built in low trees and bushes. The nests are bulky and cupshaped, made out of twigs, grasses and vines. They are usually lined with leaves and feathers. Two to five beautiful greenish-blue eggs are laid each season. The female incubates the eggs for fourteen days and broods the chicks. Both parents feed the nestlings and the male guards the nest from intrusion by predators.

Although protected as song birds, mockingbirds were once widely kept as cage birds. Pugnacious in disposition, they should not be housed in aviaries with birds which are smaller as the smaller birds will sooner or later be killed. These birds are beneficial in gardens and parklands as many insects are controlled by them.

Daily Diet for: Mockingbird (*Mimus polyglottos*); **Blue Mockingbird** (*Melanotis caerulescens*); **Hood Island Mockingbird** (*Nesomimus macdonaldi*); **Brown Thrasher** (*Toxostoma rufum*); **California Thrasher** (*Toxostoma redivivum*); **and Grey Catbird** (*Dumetella carolinensis*)

Insects: 14g mealworms, ant eggs, lawn moths, grasshoppers, May Beetles, Green June Beetles, spiders or crickets.
Fruit and berries: 5g avocado, papaya, figs, grapes, raisins (soaked overnight in water), diced apple, pyracantha, cotoneaster, eugenia, blackberries or strawberries.
Egg: 28g hard-boiled, grated and crumbled.
Mockingbird Food Mix: 5g; or Purina Trout Chow, mixed with egg.
Vegetables: 5g sauerkraut, tomato seeds, fresh corn on the cob or canned corn.
Seeds: 5g milo maize, canary millet, wild bird seeds.
Minerals: 5g Vionate multivitamin powder sprinkled on hard-boiled egg *or* 2 drops cod liver oil or wheat germ oil on a small piece of bread daily.

Orioles

The Forest Orioles or the Old World Orioles, family Oriolidae, are a small group of twenty-eight species, found in Eurasia, Africa, the East Indies, Philippine Islands and Australia. They are brightly coloured birds, chiefly yellow, green or scarlet and black. The sexes differ in colour. They measure from 20 to 30 cm in length.

The orioles of the Old World are not closely related to the New World orioles. They are closer anatomically to the crow and jay group. The English word 'oriole' is derived from the Latin word *aureolus*, meaning 'yellow' or 'golden'.

Orioles are strong, fast fliers, moving in undulatory flight, similar to that of woodpeckers. The wings are long and pointed, the tails long. The bill is strong and pointed and slightly hooked. The legs are short and stout. All have twelve tail feathers and ten primaries in the wings.

They eat many spiders and soft-bodied insects, especially woolly caterpillars, which they pound against the branches in order to remove the fuzz before swallowing. Fruits such as cherries, mulberries, currants, loquats and figs are eaten in large quantities.

Orioles weave long, hanging cradle-shaped nests in forks of trees. They are securely fastened with roots, hair and fibres which are skilfully woven. Both sexes participate in the building of the nest. Three or four white eggs, strikingly speckled with dark reddish-brown at the larger end, are laid. The incubation period is fifteen to sixteen days and the nestlings fledge at two to three weeks of age. The female alone incubates the eggs and broods the chicks. Both parents feed and care for the young.

The New World oriole's family, Icteridae, is a large one with eighty-eight species, including the blackbirds, grackles, cowbirds, meadowlarks, bobolinks, troupials, oropendolas and caciques. None of these distinctive groups is truly representative of the entire family. The New World orioles are most closely related to the Western hemisphere tanagers.

The birds in this family are medium-sized birds measuring 15 to 53 cm in length. They have rounded tails, with eight primaries. Their bills are hard, pointed and conical. In the orioles and grackles, the bill is slender and down-curved. The oropendolas and caciques have heavier bills. The meadowlark's bill is sharp and straight, while the cowbird and bobolink bills are short and finch-like.

Icterids are found in all upland habitats. Various species inhabit almost every type of forest from conifers to tropical jungles. Open fields and prairies are the home of the meadowlark and bobolink. Blackbirds inhabit marshy areas. Scott's Oriole is at home in desert country among yuccas and agaves.

All of the birds eat insects and most of them eat seeds and grains. The tropical orioles and oropendolas are fruit-eaters, with the caciques. The grackles eat bird eggs, nestlings (ibis and herons in Florida), reptiles and amphibians.

Orioles, oropendolas and caciques weave neat, hanging nests with the entrance at the top. Cowbirds practise brood parasitism, laying their eggs in other birds' nests. Grackles and blackbirds build open cup nests in trees and marshy vegetation, in colonies. Meadowlarks nest on the ground in upland grassland fields, as do bobolinks.

Two to six eggs, varicoloured and spotted, are laid by most members in this family. Incubation periods range from eleven to eighteen days. Females incubate the eggs and brood the young. Both sexes feed and care for the chicks after they are hatched.

Daily Diet for: Golden Oriole (*Oriolus oriolus*); **Black-naped Oriole** (*Oriolus chinensus*); **Maroon Oriole** (*Oriolus traillii*); **Yellow Figbird** (*Sphecotheres flaviventris*); **Black-headed Oriole** (*Icterus graduacauda*); **Scott's Oriole** (*Icterus parisorum*); **Orchard Oriole** (*Icterus spurius*); **Hooded Oriole** (*Icterus cucullatus*); **Baltimore (Northern) Oriole** (*Icterus galbula*); **Bullock's Oriole** (*Icterus bullockii*); **Spotted-breasted Oriole** (*Icterus pectoralis*); **Montezuma Oropendola** (*Psarocolius montezuma*); **Chestnut-headed Oropendola** (*Psarocolius wagleri*); **Troupial** (*Icterus icterus*); **and Yellow-rumped Cacique** (*Cacicus cela*)

Choice of fruits: 14 g thick slices of oranges, apples, pears, figs, papaya, loquats, cherries and apricots *or* $\frac{1}{2}$ can fruit cocktail or diced fruits, together with choice of mulberries, blackberries, raisins (soaked overnight in water) eugenia or pyracantha berries (4–5).
Boiled rice: 5 g.
Hard-boiled egg: 14 g, in slices.
Vegetables: 5 g grated carrots sprinkled on rice.
Purina Trout Chow: 5 g mixed with rice.
Insects: 5 g crickets, mealworms (4–5), caterpillars, beetles, moths, or spiders (2–3).
Minerals: 5 g Vionate multivitamin powder sprinkled on egg.

Daily Diet for: Red-rumped Cacique (*Cacicus haemorrhous*); Brewer's Blackbird (*Euphagus cyanocephalus*); Yellow-headed Blackbird (*Xanthocephalus xanthocephalus*); and Red-winged Blackbird (*Agelaius phoenicus*)

Fruit: 14g sliced papaya, figs, apples, oranges and pears.
Seeds: 14g milo maize, millet, cracked corn, wheat or rice.
Insects: 5g crickets or mealworms (3–4) or choice of earthworms, grubs, moths, grasshoppers or beetles.
Egg: 28g hard-boiled egg, crumbled.
Trout Chow: 5g moistened and mixed with egg.
Bread: 2g in small pieces.
Minerals: 5g Vionate multivitamin powder sprinkled on fruit.
Oyster shell: free choice.

Daily Diet for: Boat-tailed Grackle (*Quiscalus major*); Common Grackle (*Quiscalus quiscula*) and Brown-headed Cowbird (*Molothrus ater*)

Fruit: 14g papaya, figs, apples, oranges or pears.
Seeds: 14g milo maize, millet, cracked corn, wheat or rice.
Meat: 5g ground meat, snails or slugs (2).
Egg: 28g hard-boiled, crumbled.
Trout Chow: 5g moistened and mixed with egg.
Bread: 2g small pieces.
Minerals: 5g Vionate multivitamin powder sprinkled on fruit.
Oyster shell: free choice.

Daily Diet for Western Meadowlark (*Sturnella neglecta*)

Seeds: 14g canary, millet or grass seeds.
Insects: 5g mealworms or crickets.
Egg: 14g hard-boiled.
Minerals: 5g Vionate multivitamin powder sprinkled on egg.
Oyster shell: free choice.
Trout Chow: 5g.

Daily Diet for Bobolink (*Dolichonyx oryzivorus*)

Seeds: 14g paddy rice or millet.

Insects: 5 g mealworms.
Egg: 14 g hard-boiled.
Trout Chow: 5 g moistened, mixed with egg.
Minerals: 5 g Vionate multivitamin powder sprinkled on egg.
Oyster shell: free choice.

Tanagers

The Tanagers in the family Thraupidae are among the most beautiful of birds. There are 223 species and they are clothed in brilliant hues of red, green, blue, black, silver and gold. The females usually resemble the males but are duller. Some are larger than a house sparrow, some are smaller than a house wren. They measure from 7 to 30 cm in length. Tanagers are a New World family, distributed from southern Alaska and Canada south to Brazil and Argentina.

They live in the upper levels of forests and brushlands, feeding on ripening fruits, berries and insects. A few follow consistent migratory routes, but the tropical species have little reason to migrate as fruits ripen all year long and insects are abundant.

The most familiar of the tanager family in North America is the brilliantly coloured Scarlet Tanager (*Piranga olivacea*), a bright red bird with black wings and tail. Another favourite is the Western Tanager (*Piranga ludoviciana*) with its red head and face, yellow body and black wings and tail. Chlorophonias, Euphonias and Callistes are often imported for cage birds. Swallow Tanagers, Magpie Tanagers, Masked Tanagers, Paradise Tanagers, Yellow-headed, Golden, Silver-throated and Yellow-bellied Tanagers are often enjoyed in collections. All of the tanagers make up in beauty and friendliness for what they lack in song.

Nests vary from flimsy shallow cups of grasses and twigs to domes of grasses, mosses and hair with side entrances used by the euphonias. One to five eggs, white or greenish with light spots, are laid. The average incubation period is thirteen to fourteen days. Only the female incubates the eggs and broods the nestlings. The male feeds the chicks along with the female after they are hatched.

We cannot stress too strongly the dangers of feeding bananas to tanagers. More deaths of tanagers are caused from bananas in the diet than for any other reason. Both ripe and green bananas seem to be very toxic for these birds.

Daily Diet for: Scarlet Tanager (*Piranga olivacea*); Western Tanager (*Piranga ludoviciana*); Blue-necked Tanager (*Tangara cyanicollis*); Golden Tanager (*Tangara arthus*); Silver-throated Tanager (*Tangara icterocephala*); Flame-faced Tanager (*Tangara parzudakii*); and Yellow-headed (Saffron-crowned) Tanager (*Tangara xanthocephala*)

Fruit: 14 g thick slices of papaya, apple, orange, grapes, figs, prunes mixed *or* ½ can fruit cocktail.

Berries: 5 g blueberries, mulberries, blackberries, eugenia, pyracantha or cotoneaster.

Insects: 5 g mealworms, crickets (3–4). *Drosophila* (fruit flies) should be released in the aviary twice daily.

Carrots: 5 g finely grated on fruit.

Trout Chow: 5 g on diced fruit.

Hard-boiled egg: 14 g, sliced.

Minerals: 5 g Vionate or any multivitamin powder sprinkled on slices of fruit.

Daily Diet for: Masked Tanager (*Tangara nigrocincta*); Blue-grey Tanager (*Thraupis episcopus*); Swallow Tanager (*Tersina viridis*); and Mountain Tanager (*Anisognathus flavinuchus*)

Fruit: 14 g sliced papaya, apple, orange, prune, grapes and figs *or* ¼ can fruit cocktail or diced fruit.

Berries: 5 g blueberries, mulberries, raisins, currants, the latter soaked overnight in water.

Insects: 5 g mealworms (3–4).

Trout Chow: 5 g mixed with egg.

Hard-boiled egg: sliced.

Minerals: 5 g Vionate or other multivitamin powder, sprinkled on berries.

Daily Diet for: Blue-crowned Chlorophonia (*Chlorophonia occipitalis*); Yellow-crowned Euphonia (*Euphonia luteicapilla*); Blue-hooded Euphonia (*Euphonia musica*) and Violaceous Euphonia (*Euphonia violacea*)

Fruit: 14 g slices of papaya, apple, orange, prunes, grapes or figs *or* ¼ can fruit cocktail.

Berries: 5 g blueberries, mulberries or raisins or currants soaked overnight in water.

Insects: 5 g mealworms. *Drosophila* released into aviary.

Trout Chow: 5 g mixed with egg.

Hard-boiled egg: 5 g crumbled with Trout Chow.

Minerals: 5 g Vionate multivitamin powder sprinkled on berries.

Larks

The seventy-five species of larks in the family Alaudidae are almost exclusively birds of the Old World. They are widely distributed in Eurasia, Africa and South America. One species, the Horned Lark (*Eremophila alpestris*), 18 cm in length, is found in North America. Two species, the Singing Bushlark (*Mirafra cheniana*) which is 32 cm in length, and the Skylark (*Alauda arvensis*) which is 18 cm in length, are found in Australia. The skylark, originally of Eurasia and Africa, was introduced and is now well established there.

All are long-legged terrestrial birds noted for singing in flight. The spectacular flight song of the courting male skylark is one of the most beautiful of natural sounds.

With the exception of the Horned Larks and the Finch Larks of Africa and India, all larks are plainly coloured in browns and greys with dark patterns of brown and black. Camouflaged plumage is important for birds that nest on the ground in open country habitats. The sexes are similar.

In size, this family measures 13 to 23 cm in length. Larks live on open grassy plains, on moors, fields, and beaches. Many are migratory. The wings are long and pointed, the legs are long. A long, straight claw is found on the hind toe. It is used as a special tool for surfacing insects and covered weed seeds for food. Examination of the stomach contents of larks show that food consists of 21 per cent insects and 79 per cent weed seeds. The bill is pointed and slightly down-curved.

Thousands of larks are netted and trapped in a number of Old World countries for food. Considered a table delicacy, many of the tiny birds are required for a meal for one family.

Most larks build an open cup-shaped nest on the ground near or under tufts of grass. Sometimes the nest is entirely in the open. Three to six speckled eggs are laid. Only the female incubates the eggs for eleven or twelve days. The male feeds the hen on the nest during incubation. Both parents feed the nestlings until they are fledged. Larks may rear two to three broods during the nesting season, depending on the abundance of insects and live food.

Larks have never been caged in aviaries to any great degree because of their sombre colouration. They will live well on a very simple diet of insectivorous food and grass seeds supplemented with a few multivitamins. The aviaries should be dry and the floor planted with clumps of Fountain Grass (*Pennisetum ruppeli*), common vetch (*Vicia angustifolia*) and verbena (*Verbena litoralis*).

Daily Diet for: Horned Lark (*Eremophila alpestris*) and Calandra Lark (*Melanocorypha calandra*)

Insects: 5 g mealworms, beetles, larvae, pupae, crickets.
Seeds: 5 g choice of oats, buckwheat, wheat, canary, millet or packaged wild bird seed.
Dog Kibble or Trout Chow: 5 g moistened with water.
Egg: 14 g hard-boiled, crumbled on dog food or Trout Chow.
Greens: 14 g sprouted oats, barley or hydroponic grass in small clay pots.
Minerals: 5 g Vionate multivitamin powder sprinkled on egg.

Honeycreepers

There are two families of honeycreepers. Coerebidae, with thirty-six species, is widely distributed through the West Indies, Central and South America. The Hawaiian Honeycreepers, Drepanididae, with twenty-two species, are small relatives of the Tanagers and Woodwarblers.

The honeycreepers in Coerebides share the habit of feeding on the nectar and pollen of flowers, as well as on berries, small seeds and insects. They are birds of the tree tops and forest edges.

Main groups in this family are the following: honeycreepers, with long curved bills and bright colours of blue, green and yellow; bananaquits, ranging in colour from black to bright yellow, which build hanging nests in the shape of a ball and with the entrance at the bottom; flower-piercers, which have curiously upturned, hooked bills that are used to pierce the corolla of flowers to secure nectar; conebills, which are dull in colour and have short, conical bills; and dacnis, which have similar bills but are brilliant in plumage.

Some of the larger species, such as the Green Honeycreeper(*Chlorophanes spiza*) which is found in Bolivia, Brazil and Peru and the Red-legged Honeycreeper (*Cyanerpes cyaneus*) from Mexico, Ecuador, Bolivia and Brazil, feed on fruits as well as nectar and insects. Both of these species build cup-shaped nests in the forks of trees and usually have two eggs which are finely speckled at the large end. The female incubates the egg for eleven or twelve days alone. Both sexes feed the nestlings.

The Red-legged Honeycreeper is a beautiful cage bird, turquoise in colour with yellow under the wings. A pair of these birds will nest easily in a canary breeding cage. A plastic strawberry basket will work successfully as a nest when fastened to the side of the cage. Small amounts of yarn, palm fibres, dog or horse hairs may be provided for nesting material. Two eggs will be laid. The cage should not be cleaned during the nesting period. A supply of small mealworms should be available as the chicks are fed on only insectivorous food for the first seven days of their life. A small container of hydramin or hummingbird nectar should be provided as liquid during the nesting season.

The family of Hawaiian honeycreepers probably developed on the islands from a central stock that reached there from the American mainland many years ago. They are small birds, measuring 10 to 20 cm in length. They have great variety in colour and the shape and length of their bills also varies greatly. They build simple nests of grass and twigs, placed in trees or in the grass. They lay two or three eggs.

More than a dozen kinds of Hawaiian honeycreepers are now considered to be rare or in danger of extinction. There is only fragmentary knowledge of the biology and the habits of these birds as little opportunity has been possible for working with and propagating them.

Daily Diet for Honeycreepers

Choice of fruits: 14 g papaya, blueberries, currants (soaked overnight in water), orange, pears *or* $\frac{1}{3}$ can fruit cocktail or diced fruits.

Insects: 5 g mealworm pupae cut in small pieces and placed on top of bread and milk. Fruit flies (*Drosophila*) released into aviary. In a breeding cage, place in small jar lid.

Bread and milk: 5 g, not too wet, crumbled.

Pound cake: 5 g crumbled on small flat container.

Hard-boiled egg: 5 g crumbled on bread and milk.

Minerals: 5 g Vionate multivitamin sprinkled on bread and milk.

Choice of blossoms: fuchsia, honeysuckle, impatiens, shrimp plant, orchids, verbena, canary-bush, azaleas, passiflora, bottlebrush, grevillea, melianthus.

Leafbirds

The leafbirds (Irenidae) are a small family of colourful birds living in south-eastern Asia. The fourteen species in the family are found from India to the Philippine Islands, south to Sumatra, Java and Borneo. They live in both mountain forests and cultivated lands. All are non-migratory, feeding on fruits, berries, buds and numerous insects. They are active, swift-flying birds and are usually to be seen in small groups in fruiting trees. Many are excellent mimics and all are fine singers.

In size they measure from 13 to 19 cm in length. Eight species are bright green in colour, marked with patterns of blue, orange, yellow and black. The four loras are smaller birds with yellow, olive-green and black body colour. The two species of fairy bluebirds have gorgeous plumage. The males have iridescent enamel-like feathers of blue and black, the females, soft green colours.

Most leafbirds build a shallow cup-shaped nest of fine roots and grasses, which is unlined. It is coated on the outside with soft fibres and spider webs to hold it together. Two to four creamy-white eggs, streaked with brown and grey, are laid. The incubation period is thirteen to fourteen days. Both sexes incubate the eggs, brood and feed the nestlings.

In captivity, fairy bluebirds build open cup-shaped nests of grasses, horse-hair and twigs in the trees in their aviary. Three eggs are usually laid. They are greenish-white in colour, marked with blotches of reddish-brown. The female only incubates the eggs for the fourteen or fifteen day incubation period. Both parents feed the chicks in the nest. Only insect food is given for the first four or five days. Later, berries, fruits and finely ground meat is carried to the nestlings. Fairy bluebirds may rear as many as three broods in a single year.

Their brilliant colour, singing ability and adaptability to confinement in small cages makes them popular house pets. In the Orient, they are enjoyed in most homes as commonly as canaries and budgerigars in North American homes.

Daily Diet for: Fairy Bluebird (*Irena puella*); Golden-fronted Leafbird (*Chloropsis aurifrons*); Orange-bellied Leafbird (*Chloropsis hardwickii*); and Common Iora (*Aegithina tiphia*)

Fruit: 14 g blueberries, figs, papaya or grapes *or* $\frac{1}{2}$ can fruit cocktail or diced fruits.

Insects: 5g mealworm pupae.

Minced meat: 5 g.
Hard-boiled egg: 5 g crumbled on minced meat.
Minerals: 5 g Vionate multivitamin powder sprinkled on meat.

Wagtails

The wagtails or pipits (Motacillidae) are a group of graceful, slender, ground-living birds. There are fifty-three species in this family. Wagtails have long tails and the characteristic in most species of an up and down wagging motion has led to their name. They are strongly marked in black and white patterns, often with much yellow.

Their bills are thin and pointed, their legs are long and the feet have elongated back toes. They resemble larks, but are more slender and have a different and more upright carriage. Their bills are very slender. They measure from 13 to 23 cm in length.

Some members of this family live singly or in pairs on or near water. Another group lives in flocks and is associated with cattle and herds of other domestic animals which disturb the insects upon which the wagtails feed. The distribution of this family is world-wide, except for the polar regions and some oceanic islands.

One special group in Africa with eight species in the genus *Macronyx* has a long hind toe and a claw 5 cm in length which is almost one-third of the length of the entire body. This special adaptation is used by the Yellow-throated Longclaw (*Macronyx croceus*), which lives south of the Sahara, for running on top of the tufted grasses of the veldt. The Pied (White) Wagtail (*Motacilla alba*), a strikingly marked black and white bird, is possibly the most commonly seen bird in England.

Wagtails may raise three successive broods in a single year. They are ground nesters. The fragile nests are made of straws, grass and rootlets and lined with feathers, hair and bits of paper. Five to six white or buff eggs, heavily spotted with brown, form a normal clutch. The incubation period varies from fourteen to sixteen days. Both sexes incubate, brood and care for the chicks.

Pipits build deep cup-shaped nests, also on the ground. These are neatly woven of fine grasses and are well hidden. Eggs may number from three to seven, buff in colour with many brown spots. The incubation period runs from twelve to sixteen days. The female alone incubates the eggs. The male feeds the female on the nest during incubation, and the chicks after they are hatched. The thirty-four species of pipits are so similar in appearance that they are difficult to identify in the field.

Daily Diet for Wagtails and Pipits

Minced meat: 5 g in wet pan.
Purina Dog Chow: 5 g mixed with rice.
Boiled rice: 5 g.
Millet: 5 g.
Hard-boiled egg: 5 g crumbled in rice.
Insects: 2 g mealworms or crickets on top of rice.
Minerals: 5 g Vionate multivitamin powder sprinkled on meat; 2 g salt sprinkled on rice.

Starlings

The large family of starlings, Sturnidae, has 110 species. They are well represented in Eurasia, Africa, India, Indo-China, Australia, New Zealand and the Pacific Islands. All are of Old World origin. The Common Starling (*Sturnus vulgaris*), a black spotted bird with a yellow bill, was introduced from Eurasia to New York City in 1890. The brown and black Common Mynah (*Acridotheres tristis*), a native of India, has been introduced to South Africa, Australia and Hawaii. Both these introductions have had unhappy results. Both have become pests and predators, feeding on native bird eggs and nestlings as well as on fruits and insects. Both are prolific breeders and several broods are raised each year when food is abundant.

As a group, starlings are aggressive, active birds of medium size, 15 to 40 cm in length. They have straight or slightly down-curved bills, strong legs and feet. While a few hop on the ground, most walk quickly with a waddling gait.

Most are dark coloured—black with glossy plumage. Some are brown or grey. Others are brightly marked with patches of white, yellow and red. Many are crested and several show prominent wattles and bare patches of skin on the face and head. They are found in all types of wooded country, agricultural lands and in cities and villages. Most species are migratory, flying in both small and large flocks. They are noisy when feeding and roosting. Many are mimics and imitate other birds' songs and calls.

Their basic diet is insects and fruit, but those associated with man take a varied diet, including bird eggs and garbage. Beneficial because they feed on so many insects and snails which are destructive to agricultural crops and pasture grasslands, starlings are protected in many countries. In Japan, the Grey Starling (*Sturnus cineraceus*), a short, stocky bird with white on the face, rump and belly, feeds exclusively on the rice stem borer which destroys the rice crops. In Eurasia and south-western Asia, the Rosy Pastor (Rose-coloured Starling) (*Sturnus roseus*) follows periodic swarms of locusts. It nests and rears young wherever these insects are abundant. In Africa, the Wattled Starlings (*Creatophora cinerea*) also control the plagues of migrating locusts and are strictly protected.

Most starlings nest in the holes of trees, cliffs and rocks. They also use belfries and towers. Others build massive colony nests like the weaver birds of Africa. One Glossy Starling (*Aplonis panayensis*) in the South Pacific weaves a long hanging purse-shaped nest in the tree tops. Three to seven white or bluish eggs, lightly spotted, are laid. The incubation period is fourteen to twenty-five days. The female incubates the eggs alone. Both sexes feed and care for the nestlings.

The oxpeckers or tick birds are also placed in this family. The Yellow-billed Oxpecker (*Buphagus africanus*) is a specialized starling associating with large animals such as the rhinoceros and the Cape buffalo. These birds have broad bills and very thick, curved claws, and they climb on the backs of large animals feeding on the abundant ticks. This group nests in holes in tall trees.

Bali has a lovely starling or mynah, the Rothschild's Grackle or Bali Mynah (*Leucopsar rothschildi*). It is snowy-white in colour with bare sky-blue skin around the eyes. The wings and tail are tipped with black. A crest of fine white feathers can be raised at will.

Among the best of all talking cage birds is the Hill Mynah (*Gracula religiosa*). It ranges from India and Sri Lanka through the oriental region. It is glossy black in colour with yellow head wattles. Eight or nine forms have been well described. They vary from 30 to 38 cm in length. Hill Mynahs travel through the forests in small noisy flocks and live largely on fruits and insects. Two species which are generally imported as talking birds are the Greater Indian Hill Mynah (*Gracula religiosa intermedia*) and the Javan Hill Mynah (*Gracula religiosa religiosa*) from Indonesia.

Nests are made in holes in trees. Two or three bluish-green eggs are laid, spotted with purple and brown. The incubation period is fourteen days. The female incubates the eggs alone. Both parents feed and care for the chicks.

The imitations of human speech by these birds are far superior to those of any parrot. Their vocal chords are more flexible and their voices may imitate men's, women's and children's voices with little effort.

Daily Diet for: Common Starling (*Sturnus vulgaris*); **Common Mynah** (*Acridotheres tristis*); **Wattled Starling** (*Creatophora cinerea*); **Rosy Pastor (Rose-coloured Starling)** (*Sturnus roseus*); **Grey Starling** (*Sturnus cineraceus*); **and Bald-headed Starling** (*Sarcops calvus*)

Starling diet 1

Fruit: 14 g halves of figs, dates, grapes or plums and slices of apple, orange, pears or bananas; *or* ⅓ can fruit cocktail or diced fruits, elderberries, eugenia, pyracantha or hawthorn berries may also be used, as may raisins which have been soaked overnight in water.

Minced meat: 5 g.

Choice of seeds: 5 g millet, canary, milo maize or wheat.

Insects: 5 g grasshoppers, crickets, mealworms or beetle pupae.

Boiled rice: 5 g.

Grated carrots: 5 g sprinkled on rice.

Hard-boiled egg: 5 g sliced.

Trout Chow: 5 g mixed with meat *or* mynah pellets may be used.

Minerals: 5 g Vionate multivitamin powder sprinkled on meat *or* 2 drops wheat germ oil may be placed on the meat.

Daily Diet for: Amethyst (Violet-backed) Starling (*Cinnyricinclus leucogaster*); **Golden-crested Mynah** (*Mino coronatus*); **Superb Starling** (*Spreo superbus*); **Royal (Golden-breasted) Starling** (*Spreo regius*); **Blue-eared Starling** (*Lamprotornis chalybaeus*); **Rüppell's Long-tailed Starling** (*Lamprotornis purpuropterus*); **Red-winged Starling** (*Onycognathus morio*); **and Yellow-billed Oxpecker** (*Buphagus africanus*)

Starling diet 2

Choice of fruits: 14 g halves of figs, dates, grapes or plums, slices of apple, orange, pears, bananas; *or* ⅓ can fruit cocktail or diced fruit, also blackberries, eugenia, elderberries, hawthorn and pyracantha and raisins which have been soaked overnight in water.

Minced meat: 5 g.

Choice of seeds: 5 g.

Insects: 5 g grasshoppers, crickets, mealworms or beetle pupae.

Boiled rice: 5 g.

Grated carrots: 5 g on rice.
Hard-boiled egg: 28 g sliced.
Trout Chow or Mynah Bird Pellets: 5 g mixed with meat.
Minerals: 5 g Vionate multivitamin powder sprinkled on meat *or* 2 drops wheat germ oil on meat.

Diet for Rothschild's Grackle or Bali Mynah (*Leucopsar rothschildi*) (Twice Daily)

Choice of fruit: 14 g banana, apple, orange, grapes and papaya—diced; *or* $\frac{1}{3}$ can fruit cocktail in corn syrup with 5 g raisins soaked overnight in water.
Gerber's Baby oatmeal in milk: 14 g *or* bread and milk which is flaky, not soggy.
Hard-boiled egg: 19 g crumbled and sprinkled on oatmeal.
Beef pellets: 5 g pieces of fresh ground beef rolled into pellets 1 cm in diameter.
Minnows: 5 g small minnows or mosquito fish, fed whole.
Insects: mealworms, crickets, cockroaches or earthworms available in a container of leaf mould.
Minerals: 5 g Vionate multivitamin powder sprinkled on egg.

Diet for Hill Mynahs (*Gracula religiosa*) (Twice Daily)

Choice of fruits: 14 g diced figs, dates, grapes, bananas, apple, orange and raisins, soaked overnight in water; *or* $\frac{1}{2}$ can fruit cocktail or diced fruits and eugenia, pyracantha, hawthorn, elderberries or mulberries.
Boiled rice with milk: 14 g rice boiled 5 minutes until fluffy.
Hard-boiled egg: 28 g crumbled on rice.
Purina Trout Chow: 14 g moistened with water and mixed with rice.
Insects: 5 g mealworms, crickets, cockroaches or grasshoppers or fresh shredded beef heart if insects are not available. (*Note:* No meat should be fed when chicks are in the nest.)
Minerals: 5 g Vionate multivitamin powder sprinkled on egg.

Sunbirds

The Old World sunbirds, Nectariniidae, invite comparison with the American hummingbirds, but the two families are in no way related. There are 116 species in the family of brightly plumaged birds which are widely spread over the forested parts of the Old World. Two characteristics separate the sunbirds from their nearest relatives: strong sexual dimorphism, with bright metallic colouration in the males, dull colouration in the females; and an eclipse or non-breeding plumage in the males of some species.

The nostrils are oval and covered. The bill, whether long or short, slender or decurved, has fine serrations near the tip—an adaptation for holding large flying insects taken as food. In all sunbirds, the tongue is tubular for two-thirds of its length, with the tip split into two forks for extracting nectar from the blossoms of flowering plants.

The primary wing feathers may be found in each rounded wing. The legs are strong and protected with scales. The toes are short with sharp toenails. Tails may be long, square or graduated, with much variation among the species.

All types of country are inhabited by sunbirds—primitive forests, clearings, parklands and dry bush areas. In Africa, where more than half of the known species live, the very brilliant species live in open areas while the duller members are inhabitants of shady and heavy forests. Some species spend much of their lives in the tree tops whereas others keep close to the ground.

Sunbirds feed on a variety of insects and on nectar, extracting the nectar both on the wing and from a perch. The fleshy pulp of soft fruits and berries is also eaten. Large blossoms and those with long tubular corollas are pierced at the base by the long pointed bills to obtain food. Several specialized sunbirds with slender, curved bills and tubular tongues are well adapted to reaching unusual flower tubes in search of nectar and they cross-pollinate the blossom at the same time. A mistletoe (*Loranthus*) in India will not fruit unless its flowers are pollinated by the Purple-rumped Sunbird (*Nectarinia zeylonica*).

Typical sunbird nests are long, hanging purse-shaped pouches constructed of matted fibres and grasses, woven together with spider webs. The nests are hung from branches in trees, seldom more than 4–4.5 m from the ground. A few species make neat, compact nests, but most nests are ragged. The bottoms of most nests are extended with loose trails of fibres and perhaps a leaf or two wedged in in order to give the appearance of a bit of accumulated rubbish. The female alone builds the nest. When she has completed the framework and moved inside to line it, the male brings plant down, hair and feathers for the lining. Upon completion, the nest is closed from the top to prevent water from running into it. A roof-like projection is woven above the side entrance and the male uses this porch to feed the female while she is sitting in the nest. The entrance usually faces the centre of the tree.

Two or three white or bluish-white eggs with brown spots and streaks are laid. The female incubates the eggs from fourteen to seventeen days. The eyes of the chicks are closed when first hatched and open on the seventh or eighth day. The male brings insectivorous food to the brooding female for the first seven days. Both parents feed the nestlings after the first week as they require additional food.

The nine species of Spiderhunters in the genus *Arachnothera*, centred in the oriental region, are also included in this family. Completely insectivorous, they are very difficult to import alive, even by air passage. The sexes are alike in colour, dressed in grey-browns, dull yellows or olive greens. They measure 15 to 20 cm in length. The Little Spiderhunter (*Arachnothera longirostris*) of Indo-China feeds exclusively on the nectar of banana blossoms and probes into the flower tubes where spiders are abundant.

We have observed their cup-shaped nests attached to the underside of banana leaves. They sew the rim of the cup to the leaf with fibres, knotting the strands on the upperside, as do the tailorbirds. The leaf forms the roof of the nest and the entrance is a hole in the side. Two eggs are usually laid. Both sexes build the nest, incubate the eggs and care for the young. We believe the incubation period is twelve to thirteen days.

Daily Diet for Sunbirds and Spiderhunters

Fruit: 21 mg orange, figs, grapes or raisins soaked overnight in water.
*Hummingbird nectar: 21 mg.
Insects: 5 g spiders, mealworms, beetles, crickets, flies, termites, midges. Fruit flies (*Drosophila*) should be released in the aviary twice daily.
Minerals: 5 g Vionate multivitamin powder sprinkled on fruit.

White-eyes

The small family of White-eyes in the family Zosteropidae contains eight-five species. These are small, dainty birds which eat insects, fruit

* Hummingbird nectar: 5.5 litres, 1 part cane sugar to 3 parts water with 9 g Super Hydramin Powder (vanilla flavour) or 116 g Gerval supplement. This should be mixed thoroughly and fed in glass or plastic feeders.

and nectar. They range from Africa across to Japan and south to the islands of the Indian Ocean and to Australia and New Zealand. They live in forest, brushlands and mangroves.

In size, they measure from 10 to 13 cm in length. All are green or olive-green with the under-parts yellow, white or grey. The sexes are alike. The bill is slender and pointed. The tail is square and the legs are short and strong.

They feed particularly on aphids, thrips, midges, fruit-flies, ants, spiders and flies found in flowering trees. The tip of the tongue is brush-tipped for collecting nectar. Fruits such as orange, pineapples, grapes and figs are pecked for the juice.

Breeding habits are similar in all species. Each pair selects a territory and builds a strong cup-size nest. It is woven out of vegetable fibres and lichens and is bound together with spider webs. The nest is lined with hair and blossoms to cushion the eggs. Two to four bluish-white eggs are laid. The incubation period is eleven to twelve days, and the female incubates the eggs alone. As soon as the chicks hatch, both parents feed and care for the young.

Daily Diet for White-eyes

Fruit: ½ orange *and* ½ small can of fruit cocktail.
*Hummingbird nectar: 22 mg. (See footnote on p. 163.)
Insects: 7 mg small beetles, moths, spiders, flies captured in insect trap.
    Aphids are abundant in well-planted aviaries. *Drosophila* released in aviary twice daily.
Minerals: 5 73 g Vionate multivitamin powder sprinkled on fruit.

Warblers

Very few warblers are kept in cages or aviaries. These birds should be kept only by individuals able to give them painstaking care and provide the specialized diets necessary to maintain them in good health and song. Most warblers are solitary, living in forests and brush lands, swamps and woodlands. They are small birds, ranging from 9 to 25 cm in length. They have slender pointed bills, rounded tails, short to medium legs. They feed largely on insects and small animal life, although the members of one group are nectar-eaters and others add fruits, berries and seeds to their diet during the fall and winter months.

Their nests are open and cup-shaped or domed. They are built in trees or shrubs, on the ground or in reeds. Eggs will number from two to ten; they are white or buffy-white and speckled with brown. The nest building is done by the female in most species. The incubation periods vary from eleven to sixteen days. The male feeds the female on the nest and both parents feed and care for the nestlings.

In Eurasia a number of warblers are kept as household pets due to their singing ability and their graceful movements. Among the best-known warblers kept in captivity are: Blackcap Warbler (*Sylvia atricapilla*); Bluethroat (*Luscinia svecica*); Garden Warbler (*Sylvia borin*); the Siberian Rubythroat (*Luscinia calliope*); the Long-tailed (Common) Tailorbird (*Orthotomus sutorius*); the Southern Emu Wren (*Stipiturus malachurus*) and the Blue Fairy Wren (Superb Wren-Warbler) (*Malurus cyaneus*).

In aviaries where warblers or other insectivorous birds are housed, commercial blacklite safety insect traps may be installed, or a series of 7-Watt bulbs may be draped across the open wire top of the aviary to attract insects into the aviary.

Daily Diet for Warblers, Tailorbirds and Fairy Wrens

Bread and milk: 5 g.
Cottage cheese: 5 g.
Lettuce: 2 g finely shredded.
Insects: 5 g mealworms, beetles, crickets, midges, thrips, flies, spiders, small moths. *Drosophila* (fruit flies) should be released into the aviary two or three times daily.
Trout Chow: 5 g mixed with cottage cheese.
Pound cake: 5 g crumbled on cottage cheese.
Minerals: 5 g Nutro multivitamin supplement.

Finches

Finches or seedeaters, with 690 species, fall conveniently into two families; the New World Fringillidae and the Old World Ploceidae. Finches are almost world-wide in distribution, with the exception of Antarctica, the Malagasy Reepublic, the Austro-Papual region and several South Pacific Islands.

Most finches are seedeaters, although many add insects to their diets during the breeding season. Green foods, berries and fruits are also eaten in season. Many are wonderful singers. They are small to medium-sized birds, measuring from 10 to 55 cm in length.

There are 315 species of New World finches, but we will touch only the better known. The Virginian Cardinal (*Richmondena cardinalis*) is found throughout the eastern half of the USA. The grey and scarlet Pyrrhuloxias (*Cardinalis sinuata*) of the south-west have a heavy conical bill which is well adapted for cracking seeds. The heavy-bodied grosbeaks and crossbills live in the pine and oak forests.

Goldfinches are found in fields and weed patches. The buntings dwell in thickets and hedgerows. The Painted Bunting (*Passerina ciris*) is North America's most colourful bird with its indigo-blue head, goldengreen back, red rump and under-parts, wings and tail tinged with red and green. The female is completely olive-green.

The towhees, large ground-feeding sparrows, have long, rounded tails. They are often seen scratching for insects and seeds in shrubbery or brush. The Rosy Finch of the western USA and Canada spends much time on the ground, digging seeds and insects from snow banks. The redpolls are small red-capped finches with black chin spots. They wander south in large flocks from the northern provinces in the winter. They feed on weed seeds in the snow-covered fields and also eat birch and alder catkins. The Lapland Longspur and Snow Bunting are birds of the Arctic tundra and are circumpolar in the north.

The fifty or more sparrows in this family include many familiar yard birds. Most are small brown-bodied birds with streaked backs and short conical beaks. Their food, mostly seeds, is obtained on or near the ground. When not nesting, most are seen in flocks.

The thirteen species of Darwin's Finches which are isolated in the Galapagos Islands and Cocos Islands have adapted their bills for the food which is available. All probably originated from a single bunting-like ancestor which came from the Central or South American mainland. Some became seedeaters with conical beaks, others became leaf and soft food eaters (fruit) with thin and delicate beaks, and others became insecteaters. The Woodpecker Finch (*Camarhynchus pallidus*) uses a tool to dig insects out of cacti and the bark of trees in the manner of woodpeckers.

The small finches known as seedeaters ranging from southern Texas to Argentina number thirty or more species. Those often seen in captivity are Hick's Seedeater, the Yellow-faced Grasquit from Mexico to Brazil, the White-throated Seedeater and the Lines Seedeater from Venezuela.

The Red-crested Cardinal (*Paroaria coronata*) found from Bolivia to Argentina and the Pope or Red-headed Cardinal (*Paroaria dominicana*) of eastern Brazil have long been popular cage and aviary birds. The Saffron Finch (*Sicalis flaveola*), a ground finch from Venezuela to Argentina, is bright yellow in colour. It is one of the few hole-nesters in the family.

The 365 species of Old World seedeaters fall into three well-marked groups. There are 112 goldfinches and allies, 107 waxbills and 156 weaver finches.

The European (Eurasian) Goldfinch (*Carduelis carduelis*), the Yellowhammer (*Emberiza citrinella*) of western Eurasia and Siberia, the colourful Chaffinch (*Fringilla coelebs*) seen in English gardens and parks and the Brambling (*Fringilla montifringilla*) of northern Eurasia and Asia all move in tremendous flocks of nomadic migrations. The European Bullfinch (*Pyrrhula pyrrhula*) with its black cap and salmon-red under-parts is a lovely finch and is popular with aviculturists. In Japan the Hawfinch (*Coccothraustes coccothraustes*) and the black and grey Japanese Grosbeak (*Eophona personata*) with its bright yellow bill are colourful finches.

The best known of all cage birds is the canary, a finch of the siskin type. Wild canaries still exist in the Canary Islands, where they were exported to Eurasia in the sixteenth century. The Wild Canary (*Serinus canaria*) is yellow-breasted with a streaked greyish-brown back. The female is dull brown in colour. Centuries of selective breeding in captivity both for colour and song have produced the many distinctive colours we enjoy today.

The second group of Old World seedeaters is the waxbills. They are distributed in Africa, southern Asia, Indonesia and Australia. They live in forest edges, open grasslands and reedy marshes. The appeal of waxbills as cage birds is due to their bright colours, and bills which look like sealing wax, and liveliness. They are ground feeders, eating small seeds, green food, berries and insects. The grass finches are also included in this group.

Red-eared Waxbills, Butterfly Finches, Orange-cheeked Waxbills, Locust Finches, Green Avadavats, Yellow-bellied Waxbills, Red Avadavats, Zebra Finches, Fire Finches, Red-browed Finches, Lavender Finches (Bluish Waxbills), St. Helena Waxbills and Crimson-winged Waxbills are welcomed for importation.

The most beautiful grass finch is the red-headed Gouldian Finch (*Chloebia gouldiae*) of Australia. With its bright red head, black throat, purple breast, yellow under-parts, green back and wings, blue rump, and black tail, it is a living 'rainbow'. White-eared Grassfinches, Masked

Finches, Black-rumped Parson Finches, and Long-tailed Finches are all popular. The Crimson (Blood) Finch (*Neochmia phaeton*) of northern Australia and New Guinea must also be listed. Star Finches, Diamond Firetails, Painted Finches and Blue-faced Parrot Finches are other outstanding Australian finches.

The thirty munias and mannikins in the genus *Lonchura* are found in Africa, across southern Asia to the Philippines and south to Australia. They are grassland birds of savannahs and rice paddies. The members of this group are considered to be pests in several countries because their large populations destroy ripening crops. The Chestnut-breasted Mannikin (*Lonchura castaneothorax*) destroys rice crops in the Philippines and Malaya. Bronze Mannikins are a problem with grain ripening in Africa. The White-crowned or headed Mannikin (*Lonchura nevermanni*) of southern New Guinea may also be a problem. All mannikins are prolific, rearing as many as five clutches each year. The well-known Java Rice Bird or Java Sparrow (*Padda oryzivora*), pearl-grey in colour with white ear patches and red bill, is a delightful cage bird, but has recently been denied importation into the USA.

The third group of Old World seedeaters comprises the weaver birds, which are divided into four subfamilies: the Buffalo Weavers (Bubalornithinae); the Sparrow Weavers (Passerinae); the Typical Weavers (Ploceinae); and the Widow (Whydah) Weavers (Viduinae).

Their greatest development is in Africa but they are also found in Eurasia, the Malagasy Republic and Malaysia. Usually found in open country, a few live in deep forests or on rocky hillsides. Seeds, vegetable matter and insects are all eaten by weaver finches.

Weavers are master architects when building their nests. Although they build nests of varying design, certain common features are found. The nest basket is built up largely from a fixed position on an initial ring and the dimensions of the nest and ante-chamber are determined by the reach of the male.

The Social Weavers (*Philetairus socius*) of South Africa build large communal structures where pairs pool their efforts and as many as 100 nests are included in the one structure.

The Buffalo Weaver (*Bubalornis albirostris*) which is 25 cm in length is a large weaver living in the drier parts of Africa. They build large untidy dome nests of thorn twigs, often a dozen in a single tree. Two or more pairs may occupy a single nest. The sharp thorns prevent any predators from disturbing the nest or eating the nestlings.

Prominent among the thirty-five Sparrow Weavers is the common

House Sparrow (*Passer domesticus*) which was introduced into the USA in 1870 from Eurasia. It is now a pest in most of the continent. The Eurasian Tree Sparrow (*Passer montanus*) which is also a pest in rice paddies was introduced into the Philippine Islands and Japan. Thousands are sold annually in the markets for food. Both of these sparrows make untidy cup-shaped nests in shrubs, vines or under the eaves of buildings.

The Typical Weavers (Ploceinae) number about 109 species. Most of them are found in Africa with a few in southern Asia. In this group the sexes are unlike. The males are bright red, orange or yellow. The females resemble female house sparrows. All weave attractive flask-like or funnel-shaped pendant nests which are entered from the bottom. Closely woven and waterproof, these nests are lined with soft material. A thorny acacia or eucalyptus tree may be completely taken over by a colony, with hundreds of nests in a single tree at the tip of each branch.

The Black-headed Village Weaver (*Ploceus cucullatus*), the Red Bishop (*Euplectes orix*), the Taveta Golden Weaver (*Ploceus castaneiceps*) of eastern Kenya, the Napolean or Yellow Bishop (*Euplectes capensis*) and the Red-billed Quelea of Dioch (*Quelea quelea*) are often seen in bird markets.

The Widow (Whydah) Weavers are parasitic. They weave no nests and use foster parents to incubate their eggs and to rear their young. They have spectacular courtship patterns. The males are polygamous, mating with several females and living in harems. During the breeding season the males grow long tail feathers, ribbon-like in appearance. They also develop colourful wing patches and body feathers. They clear dancing arenas in tall grasses, sometimes 1 to 1.2 m in diameter. A single clump of tall grass is left in the centre of the arena. Around this the male prances, spreads his tail feathers and makes vertical courtship flights to attract females.

The Long-tailed Widowbird (*Euplectes progne*) of central and western Kenya is jet black with a neck ruff and red and buff wing patches. Its tail is 60 cm in length. It is one of the most striking of the African birds.

The Paradise Whydah (*Vidua paradisea*) of east Africa and Fischer's Whydah (*Vidua fischeri*) from Somalia to Tanzania are popular aviary birds. The Paradise Whydah lays its eggs in the nest of the Melba Finch (Green-winged Pytilia) (*Pytilia melba*) as its parasitic host. Fischer's Whydah parasitizes the nest of the Purple Grenadier (*Uraeginthus ianthinogaster*).

Daily Diet for: Virginian Cardinal (*Richmondena cardinalis*); Pyrrhuloxia (*Cardinalis sinuata*); Red-crested Cardinal (*Paroaria coronata*); and Red-headed (Pope) Cardinal (*Paroaria dominicana*)

Seeds: 14 g sunflower, canary, millet or hemp.
Greens: 5 g chickweed, dandelion, sour dock, spinach, sweet alyssum, parsley, sow thistle, swiss chard.
Eggs: 5 g hard-boiled eggs, sliced.
Insects: 5 g mealworms, beetles, pupae, crickets, cotton worm, grasshopper, small moths.
Minced meat: 5 g.
Fruit: 14 g sliced apple *or* $\frac{1}{3}$ can fruit cocktail or diced fruit. Berries in season—hawthorn, mulberries, pyracantha or elderberries.
Minerals: 5 g Vionate multivitamin powder sprinkled on meat.

Daily Diet for: Yellow Grosbeak (*Pheucticus chrysopeplus*); Rose-breasted Grosbeak (*Pheucticus ludovicianus*); Evening Grosbeak (*Coccothraustes vespertina*); Blue Grosbeak (*Passerina caerulea*); White-winged Grosbeak (*Coccothraustes carnipes*); Japanese Grosbeak (*Eophona personata*); Hawfinch (*Coccothraustes coccothraustes*); Bullfinch (*Pyrrhula pyrrhula*); Buff-throated Saltator (*Saltator maximus*); White-winged Crossbill (*Loxia leucoptera*); Pine Grosbeak (*Pinicola enucleator*); and Black-headed Grosbeak (*Pheucticus melanocephalus*)

Seeds: 14 g sunflower, shelled peanuts, pine nuts.
Greens: 5 g chickweed, dandelion, sour dock, spinach, sweet alyssum, parsley, sow thistle or swiss chard.
Egg: 5 g hard-boiled, sliced.
Insects: 5 g mealworms, beetles, crickets, cotton worm, grasshoppers, small moths. Potato beetles may be fed to Rose-breasted Grosbeak.
Minced meat: 5 g.
Fruit: 14 g sliced apple or canned fruit cocktail. Berries in season may be fed: hawthorn, mulberry, pyracantha and elderberry.
Minerals: 5 g Vionate multivitamin powder sprinkled on meat.

Daily Diet for Buntings

Seeds: 5 g canary or yellow millet.

Greens: 14 g chickweed, dandelion, shepherd's purse, sow thistle or sweet alyssum.
Insects: 5 g mealworms, pupae.
Pound cake: 5 g crumbled and mixed with egg.
Egg: 14 g hard-boiled, crumbled.
Minerals: 5 g Vionate multivitamin powder sprinkled on egg.

The above diet is used for Painted Bunting (*Passerina ciris*); Lazuli Bunting (*Passerina amoena*); Indigo Bunting (*Passerina cyanea*); Yellow hammer (*Emberiza citrinella*); Red-headed Bunting (*Emberiza bruniceps*); Yellow-breasted Bunting (*Emberiza aureola*); and Brambling (*Fringilla montifringilla*).

Daily Diet for: Chaffinch (*Fringilla coelebs*); Greenfinch (*Carduelis chloris*); European Goldfinch (*Carduelis carduelis*); American Goldfinch (*Carduelis tristis*); Lawrence's Goldfinch (*Carduelis lawrencei*); and Dickcissel (*Spiza americana*)

Seeds: 14 g choice of canary, millet, hemp, thistle, rape, teasel, maw, dry oat cereal.
Greens: 14 g choice of chickweed, sow thistle, shepherd's purse, sweet alyssum, dandelion and golden ragwort.
Egg: 5 g sliced hard-boiled egg, crumbled.
Pound cake: 5 g crumbled and mixed with egg.
Insects: 5 g mealworms, pupae or crickets.
Minerals: 5 g Vionate multivitamin powder sprinkled on egg.

Note: Floor of aviary should be sodded.

Daily Diet for Grey Singing Finch (*Serinus leocopygius*) and Green Singing Finch (Yellow-fronted Canary) (*Serinus mozambicus*)

Seeds: 5 g choice of canary, spray millet, thistle, rape or teasel.
Greens: 5 g choice of chickweed, watercress, sow thistle or sweet alyssum.
Bread: 5 g dry, in cubes.
Insects: 5 g choice of flies, mealworms, beetles, small caterpillars.
Hard-boiled egg: 14 g crumbled.
Minerals: 5 g Vionate multivitamin powder sprinkled on egg.

Daily Diet for Canary (*Serinus canaria*)

Seeds: 5 g mixture of 2 parts canary seed with 1 part rape.
Greens: 5 g shepherd's purse, chickweed, dandelion or lettuce in seed.
Bread: 5 g dry, cubed.
Hard-boiled egg: 14 g crumbled.
Minerals: 5 g Vionate multivitamin powder sprinkled on egg.

Daily Diet for Red Siskin (*Carduelis cucullatus*)

Seeds: 5 g millet spray or yellow millet.
Bread: 5 g dry, cubed.
Hard-boiled egg: 14 g crumbled.
Minerals: 5 g Vionate multivitamin powder sprinkled on egg.

Note: Aviary should be sodded.

Daily Diet for Saffron Finch (*Sicalis flaveola*)

Seeds: 5 g choice of canary, millet, dry oat cereal.
Bread: 5 g dry, cubed.
Hard-boiled egg: 14 g, crumbled.
Minerals: 5 g Vionate multivitamin powder sprinkled on egg.

Note: Aviary should be sodded.

Daily Diet for Orange-billed Sparrow (*Arremon aurantiirostris*)

Seed: 5 g choice of canary, millet or oat groats.
Bread: 5 g dry, cubed.
Hard-boiled egg: 14 g, crumbled.
Vitamins: 5 g Vionate multivitamin powder sprinkled on egg.

Note: Aviary should be sodded.

Daily Diet for: House Sparrow (*Passer domesticus*); Eurasian Tree Sparrow (*Passer montanus*); and White-crowned Sparrow (*Zonotrichia leucophrys*)

Seeds: 5 g choice of canary, millet, milo, wild bird seed or sunflower.
Bread: 5 g dry, cubed.
Hard-boiled egg: 14 g crumbled.
Minerals: 5 g Vionate multivitamin powder sprinkled on egg.

Note: Aviary should be sodded.

Daily Diet for: Golden-crowned Sparrow (*Zonotrichia atricapilla*); White-throated Sparrow (*Zonotrichia albicollis*); Fox Sparrow (*Zonotrichia iliaca*); Song Sparrow (*Zonotrichia melodia*); Oregon (Western) Junco (*Junco oreganus*); and Slate-coloured Junco (*Junco hyemalis*)

Seeds: 14 g choice of canary, millet, milo, sunflower, oats, wheat, wild bird seed.
Greens: 5 g sprouted oats, wheat or barley.
Hard-boiled egg: 14 g sliced.
Bread: 5 g crumbs.
Insects: 5 g choice of mealworms, beetles, crickets or small moths or flies.
Minerals: 5 g Vionate multivitamin powder sprinkled on egg.

Daily Diet for: Brown Towhee (*Pipilo fuscus*); Spotted (Rufussided) Towhee (*Pipilo erythrophthalmus*); and House Finch (*Carpodacus mexicanus*)

Seeds: 14 g choice of canary, millet, milo, sunflower, oats, wheat, or wild bird seed.
Fruit: 5 g strawberries, blackberries, cherries or grapes in season.
Hard-boiled egg: 14 g sliced.
Bread: 5 g crumbs.
Insects: 5 g choice of mealworms, beetles, crickets, moths, flies.
Minerals: 5 g Vionate multivitamin powder sprinkled on egg.

Daily Diet for: Gouldian Finch (*Chloebia gouldiae*); Crimson (Blood) Finch (*Neochmia phaeton*); Blue-faced Parrot Finch (*Erythrura trichroa*); Melba Finch (Green-winged Pytilia) (*Pytilia melba*); Purple Grenadier (*Uraeginthus ianthinogaster*); Green Avadavat (*Amandava formosa*); Red-cheeked Cordon Bleu (*Uraeginthus bengalus*); Locust Finch (*Ortygospiza locustella*); and Zebra Finch (*Poephila guttata*)

Seeds: 5 g canary, millet, millet sprays, blue maw, niger.
Greens: 5 g chickweed, dandelion, spinach, beet leaves, shepherd's purse, ragwort (groundsel).
Insects: 5 g mealworms, pupae.
Pound cake: 5 g.

Hard-boiled egg: 5 g mixed with pound cake crumbs.
Minerals: 5 g Vionate multivitamin powder sprinkled on egg.
Charcoal: free choice.

Daily Diet for: Red Avadavat or Strawberry Finch (*Amandava amandava*); African Firefinch (*Lagonosticta rubricata*); Cut-throat (Ribbon) Finch (*Amadina fasciata*); Red-browed Finch (Sidney Waxbill) (*Aegintha temporalis*); Cherry (Plum-headed) Finch (*Aidemosyne modesta*); Masked Finch (*Poephila personata*); Black-rumped Parson Finch (*Poephila cincta atropygialis*); Diamond Fire-tail Finch (*Emblema guttata*); Painted Finch (*Emblema picta*); and Star Finch (*Neochmia ruficauda*)

Seeds: 5 g canary, yellow millet, spray millet.
Greens: 5 g chickweed, New Zealand spinach.
Insects: 5 g mealworms.
Hard-boiled egg: 5 g sliced.
Bread crumbs: 5 g sprinkled on egg.
Minerals: 5 g Vionate multivitamin powder sprinkled on egg.

Daily Diet for: White-crowned Mannikin (*Lonchura nevermanni*); Java Sparrow (*Padda oryzivora*); Bronze (Bronze-winged) Mannikin (*Lonchura cucullata*); Black-headed Nun (Chestnut Mannikin) (*Lonchura malacca*); Buffalo Weaver (*Bubalornis albirostris*); Social Weaver (*Philetairus socius*); Red-billed Quelea (*Quelea quelea*); and Black-headed Village Weaver (*Ploceus cucullatus*)

Seeds: 5 g canary, brown millet, millet sprays, dry oat cereal.
Bread crumbs: 5 g wheat bread.
Insects: 5 g mealworms, pupae.
Trout Chow: 5 g moistened and mixed with bread crumbs.
Minerals: 5 g Vionate multivitamin powder sprinkled on greens.

Daily Diet for: Red Bishop (*Euplectes orix*); Yellow Bishop (*Euplectes capensis*); Taveta Golden Weaver (*Ploceus castaneiceps*); Black-necked Weaver (*Ploceus nigricollis*); Javan Manyar (Streaked) Weaver (*Ploceus manyar*); Fire-fronted Weaver (Bishop) (*Euplectes diadematus*); Southern Grenadier Weaver (*Euplectes afer taha*); and Baya Weaver (*Ploceus philippinus*)

Seeds: 5 g canary, millet sprays hung on sides of aviary.
Greens: 5 g chickweed, watercress, sprouted oats on aviary floor.

Bread crumbs: 5 g wheat bread.
Insects: 5 g mealworms.
Trout Chow: 5 g moistened, mixed with bread crumbs.
Minerals: 5 g Vionate multivitamin powder sprinkled on greens.

Daily Diet for: Paradise Whydah (*Vidua paradisea*); Pintail Whydah (*Vidua macroura*); Long-tailed Widowbird (*Euplectes progne*); Jackson's Widowbird (*Euplectes jacksoni*); Fischer's Whydah (*Vidua fischeri*); Red-collared Widowbird (*Euplectes ardens*); White-winged Widowbird (*Euplectes albonotatus*); and Queen Whydah (*Vidua regia*)

Seeds: 14 g sunflower, hemp, canary or large millet.
Greens: 14 g choice of swiss chard, sow thistle, dock, spinach, beet tops. Whole plants of dandelion or comfrey may be hung in aviary on sides or in metal containers by perches.
Purina Trout Chow: 5 g moistened and mixed with bread crumbs.
Bread crumbs: 5 g whole wheat bread.
Insects: 5 g mealworms.
Minerals: 5 g Vionate multivitamin powder sprinkled on Trout Chow.

FEEDING AND ATTRACTING
WILD BIRDS IN GARDENS

The feeding and attracting of wild birds is a pastime long enjoyed by people in all parts of the world. In recent years, commercial feed mixtures have been developed and are available in food markets, pet shops and plant nurseries. Many pleasant hours can come from watching birds in our patios and gardens.

There is a grave responsibility associated with bird feeding. In the winter months, if feeding is initiated it must be continued until spring, in order to eliminate hazards to dependent populations of birds. A daily supply of food must be maintained when natural food has disappeared in order to keep the birds from starving.

Bird baths are enjoyed by most birds and in very hot weather a source of water will attract many birds. These baths should be cleaned regularly to prevent mosquito breeding. Many small birds are attracted to lawn sprinklers. Keeping lawns and other areas well watered increases the food supply, such as earthworms, grubs and other insects. A bit of water in other places may supply the mud needed by robins and swallows for building their nests. Other birds need dusting areas. Turning the soil at the base of a sunny wall will provide sites for dust baths.

Various types of food may be placed in feeders: millet, cracked corn, sunflower, milo, peanuts, oats, rice, figs, blackberries, strawberries, slices of apple, oranges, grapes and raisins are some examples.

Animal fats are standard food for woodpeckers, warblers, titmice and nuthatches. Suet of either beef or mutton is eaten well during the cold winter months in most regions. Various other foods may be enjoyed also. Breadcrumbs, crackers, cheese, hard-boiled eggs, dog biscuits, cereals, pound cake, pumpkin seeds, squash seeds and peanut butter on pieces of bread are suggested. In the springtime baked, crushed eggshells will supply additional calcium. This is particularly helpful during the breeding season.

In the USA, sugar water or nectar is enjoyed by hummingbirds, orioles and other fruit-eating birds. This is fed in glass or plastic feeders. One part of table sugar to three parts of water, mixed thoroughly before placing in the feeder, is given. Many types of feeders are manufactured and offered for sale in plant nurseries, pet shops and variety stores.

One of the secrets of a bird-feeding programme is to use simple, unpainted feeders in locations near vegetation where birds repeatedly perch. A shallow wooden tray, divided into compartments with various types of food, will attract different birds. A pine cone, spread with peanut butter and hung from a tree branch is another suggestion. Pieces of suet, held to a tree trunk by 1-cm wire mesh, will also prove attractive.

Another method of making food available is to plant trees, shrubs and herbs that produce seeds and fruits and let the birds reap their harvest in their own way.

APPENDIX I
Composition of Commercial Foods, Food Additives and Vitamin Compounds

Additives

Gevral

Protein—60%
Fat—Not more than 2%
Carbohydrate—24.2%
Vitamin A Palmitate—2.167 USP (United States Pharmocopeia XI) units
(54% MDR—minimum daily requirement)
(Analysis by Lederle Laboratories, Inc., Pearl River, New York.)

Super Hydramin Powder

65% Protein
0.25% Fat
0.6% Fibre
5.0% Moisture
6.6% Ash
22.45% Carbohydrates
Vitamins—A, B_{12}
(Manufactured by Nion Corporation, Inc., 1000 N. Highland Ave., Los Angeles, Ca 90038.)

Commercial Foods

Fruit Cocktail: Canned Diced Fruit (248 g)

Ingredients
Diced peaches, cherries, grapes, pineapple, sugar in heavy syrup.

[178]

Contents
Protein—1 g per cup serving
Carbohydrates—46 g per cup serving
Vitamin A—8%
Vitamin C—8%
Thiamin—2%
Riboflavin—2%
Niacin—4%
Calcium—0%
Iron—2%
Phosphorus—2%
Magnesium—2%.

Game Bird Starter Crumble

Ingredients
Ground yellow corn, ground milo, ground barley, wheat bran, ground oats, fish meal, meat, bone meal, soybean meal, cottonseed meal, condensed fish solubles, machine dehydrated kelp, fish glandular hydrolyseate, alfalfa leaf meal, dehydrated alfalfa meal, ribo-fish flour, hydrolysed defatted fish liver, choline chloride, riboflavin supplement, manganese sulphate, dried skim milk, ground shell, salt, Vitamin A and D feeding oil, Vitamin B_{12}, Vitamin K.

Guaranteed Analysis
Crude Protein, not less than 30%
Crude Fat, not less than 3.5%
Crude Fibre, not more than 5%
Ash, not more than 10%
Added Minerals, not more than 2%
(Manufactured by O. H. Kruse, Grain & Milling Co., 1459 Santa Ana Ave., El Monte, Ca 91731, USA.)

Mealworms (from commercial sources, on a per cent dry basis)

Protein—7.98%
Fat—26.24%
Carbohydrate—57.57%
Moisture—5.49%
Ash—2.72%.

Gas chromatography identified eleven fatty acids of lyophilized and esterfied specimens. Automatic analyses of hydrolized specimens gave amounts of twenty amino acids. Chemical and microbiological assays were made for vitamins A, C, E, thiamin, riboflavin, niacin, folic acid, B_6 and B_{12}. Mineral contents were determined by AOAC (American Organization of Analytical Chemistry) methods and atomic absorption spectrophotometry.

Purina Dog Chow

Ingredients
Meat and bone meal, wheat germ meal, ground oat groats, ground yellow corn, ground grain sorghums, wheat middlings, ground wheat, soybean meal, cereal food, dried whey, animal fat preserved with butylated hydroxyanisole, vitamin B_{12} supplement, artificial colouring, pyridoxine hydrochloride, riboflavin supplement, brewers' dried yeast, vitamin A supplement, D activated plant sterol, vitamin E supplement, thiamin, niacin, iodized salt, manganese sulphate, mangamous oxide, zinc oxide, iron oxide, copper oxide, cobalt carbonate.

Composition
Protein—23.8%
Fat—9.4%
Fibre—3.7%
*NFE (Nitrogen-Free Extract) (by difference)—47.5%
Gross Energy—K cal/g—4.36%
(Manufactured by Ralston Purina Co., St Louis, Mo. 63188.)

Purina Game Bird F & M (Flight and Maintenance) Chow

Ingredients
Ground yellow corn, ground milo and grain sorghums, soybean meal, dried whey, dehydrated alfalfa meal preserved with ethoxyquin, wheat middlings, vitamin A supplement, D activated animal sterol, vitamin E supplement, riboflavin, vitamin B_{12} supplement, calcium pantothenate, niacin, calcium carbonate, deflourinated phosphate, iodized salt, manganous oxide, choline chloride, zinc oxide, menadione sodium bisulphate (source of vitamin K activity).

---

*NFE: the difference between 100% and the sum of the percentages of moisture, protein, fat, fibre and ash. It is considered to represent the carbohydrates other than fibre.

Composition
Protein—19%
Fat—2.5%
Fibre—12%
NFE—40%
Ash—9%

Purina Pigeon Chow Checkers

Ingredients
Ground yellow corn or grain sorghums, soybean meal, dried whey, de-hydrated alfalfa meal, wheat middlings, vitamin A supplement, D acti-vated animal sterol, vitamin E supplement, riboflavin supplement, vita-min B_{12} supplement, calcium pantothenate, niacin, calcium carbonate, deflourinated phosphate, iodized salt, manganous oxide, choline chloride, zinc oxide, menadione sodium bisulphate.

Composition
Protein—15%
Fat—2.5%
Fibre—6.0%
NFE—56%
Ash—2.5%

Purina Pullet Developer

Ingredients
Ground grain sorghums, soybean meal, wheat mill run, dehydrated alfalfa meal, dechlorinated phosphate, calcium carbonate, iodized salt, meat and bone meal, ethoxyquin methionine hydroxy analogue calcium, vitamin B_{12} supplement, riboflavin supplement, niacin, manganous oxide, copper sulphate, zinc oxide, calcium pantothenate, choline chloride, vitamin K, vitamin A supplement, D activated animal sterol, folic acid.

Composition
Crude Protein—not less than 13%
Crude Fat, not less than 2.5%
Crude Fibre—not more than 6.0%
Ash—not more than 8%
Added Minerals, not more than 4%

Purina Trout Chow

Ingredients

Fish meal, soybean meal, ground wheat, brewers' dried yeast, ground yellow corn, wheat middlings, dried whey, animal fat preserved with BHA (chemical preservatives, propylene glycolipropyl gallate and citric acid), dicalcium phosphate, iodized salt, vitamin A supplement, D activated animal sterol (D_3), menadione dimethylpyrimidinol bisulphate (K), methionine hydroxy analogue calcium, vitamin E supplement, vitamin B_{12} supplement, ascorbic acid, biotin, choline chloride, folic acid, pyridoxine hydrochloride, thiamin, niacin, calcium pantothenate, riboflavin supplement, copper oxide, manganous oxide, iron oxide, zinc oxide, calcium carbonate, cobalt carbonate.

Composition

Crude Protein—not less than 40%
Crude Fat—not less than 4%
Crude Fibre—not more than 5.5%
Ash—not more than 13%; minerals—not more than 3%

Purina Rabbit Chow

Ingredients

Ground yellow corn, dehydrated alfalfa meal, wheat middlings, ground oats, oat mill by-products, soybean meal, cane molasses, vitamin B_{12} supplement, D activated plant sterol, vitamin E supplement, vitamin A supplement, calcium carbonate, dicalcium phosphate, monosodium phosphate, calcium pantothenate, choline chloride, folic acid, niacin, pyridoxine, hydrochloride, iodized salt, iron oxide, manganous oxide, copper oxide, cobalt carbonate, zinc oxide, riboflavin supplement, methionine hydroxy analogue calcium.

Composition

Protein—16%
Fat—2.5% (minimum)
Fibre—18% (maximum)
Ash—7.3%
Calcium—0.91%
Potassium—1.19%

Turkey Grow Ration

Ingredients
Ground milo, ground corn, wheat bran, meat and bone and blood meal, cottonseed meal, alfalfa meal, safflower meal, fish meal, fish solubles, cane molasses, ground shell flour, salt, vitamin mix, vitamin B_{12}, D activated animal sterols, vitamin A acetate, yeast culture, fish liver and glandular meal, condensed fish solubles, dried milk, albumen, manganese sulphate, wheat germ meal, wheat germ oil, riboflavin, calcium pantothenate, choline chloride, niacin, methionine.

Composition
Crude Protein—not less than 24%
Crude Fat—not less than 3.5%
Crude Fibre—not more than 6%
Ash—not more than 10%
Added minerals—not more than 2.5%
(Manufactured by O. H. Kruse Grain & Milling Co., El Monte, Ca 91734.)

ZuPreem Bird of Prey Diet

Ingredients
Horse meat, horse meat by-products, meat by-products, chicken, fresh liver, ground corn, ground wheat, fish meal, dried whole egg, dicalcium phosphate, brewers' dried yeast, iodized salt, choline chloride, vitamin A palmitate, carolene, D activated sterol, a-tocopherol, menadione, niacin, calcium pantothenate, thiamin, riboflavin, pyridoxine hydrochloride, folic acid, biotin, vitamin B_{12} supplement, ferrous carbonate, manganous oxide, zinc oxide, copper oxide, cobalt carbonate, magnesium oxide.

Composition
Crude Protein—18% (min)
Crude Fat—5% (min)
Crude Fibre—0.5% (min)
Dry Matter—40% (min)
Moisture—60% (max)
Ash—4% (max)
Calcium—0.4% (min)—0.8% (max)
Phosphorus—0.3% (min)
(Manufactured by Hill's Division, Riviana Foods Inc., PO Box 148, Topeka, Kansas 66601.)

ZuPreem Ratite Diet

Ingredients
Ground corn, soy grits, wheat, oats, dehydrated alfalfa meal, meat and bone meal, dried skimmed milk, fish meal, whole egg, animal fat, dicalcium phosphate, brewers' yeast, calcium oxide, iodized salt, potassium, vitamin A palmitate, thiamin, vitamin B_{12}.

Composition
Crude Protein—21% (min)
Crude Fat—3.5% (min)
Crude Fibre—7% (max)
Moisture—10% (max)
Ash—10% (max)
Calcium—2.5%
Phosphorus—1.0% (min)
(Manufactured by Riviana Foods Inc., PO Box 148, Topeka, Kansas 66601.)

ZuPreem Soft-Billed Bird Diet

Ingredients
Meat by-products, soy flour, sugar, corn flour, casein, liver, animal fat, ground wheat, dried whole egg, brewers' dried yeast, propylene glycol, dicalcium phosphate, fish meal, steamed bone meal, calcium carbonate, grit, iodized salt, potassium sorbate, choline chloride, flamin oil, iron carbonate, manganous oxide, zinc oxide, magnesium oxide, copper oxide, cobalt carbonate, vitamin A palmitate, D activated animal sterol, atocopherol, menadione sodium bisulfite complex, niacin, calcium pantothenate, thiamin, pyridoxine hydrochloride, vitamin B_{12} supplement, riboflavin, folic acid, biotin, methylparaben, propylparaben, BHA in propylene glycol, and water to process properly.

Composition
Crude Protein—20% (min)
Crude Fat—13% (min)
Crude Fibre—1.5% (max)
Moisture—23% (max)
Ash—7% (max)
Calcium—1.0% (min)
Phosphorus—0.6% (min)
(Manufactured by Riviana Foods Inc., Topeka, Kansas 66601.)

Wheat Hearts

Ingredients
Wheat flour, ground wheat and wheat germ meal.

Composition
Crude Protein, not less than 14.2%
Crude Fat, not less than 3.3%
Crude Fibre, not more than 5.4%
NFE, not less than 70.7%
Ash, not more than 1.4%
(Manufactured by General Mills Co.)

Composition of Common Seeds (percentages)

Seed	Moisture	Protein	Fat	Fibre	Ash	NFE
Millet Spray	9.93	12.77	3.27	8.95	3.78	62.30
Millet	11.76	14.50	5.56	11.24	5.50	51.44
Canary	14.30	13.67	3.52	21.29	9.99	37.25
Wheat	10.52	11.87	2.09	1.70	1.83	71.90
Oats	9.96	12.07	4.42	11.92	3.35	58.28
Rice	11.68	8.09	1.80	8.89	5.02	64.52
Milo	12.36	12.11	3.63	2.39	1.43	68.08
Corn	13.06	8.61	3.84	1.93	1.31	71.25
Buck-Wheat	12.62	10.02	2.24	8.67	2.02	64.23
Rape	7.30	19.54	45.00	5.95	4.21	17.99
Niger	7.02	19.37	43.22	14.33	3.48	12.37
Sunflower	6.88	15.19	28.29	28.54	3.20	17.36
Anise	12.78	18.12	11.60	13.35	8.20	33.45
Fennel	17.19	16.28	11.75	13.74	8.60	32.34
Caraway	8.90	21.45	16.53	16.34	7.39	29.39
Poppy	4.22	21.10	50.02	5.40	6.86	9.96
Hemp	8.75	21.51	30.41	18.84	4.60	15.89
Sesame	5.61	21.12	46.78	5.08	6.02	18.63
Peanut	13.15	27.95	35.77	3.04	2.36	17.73
Flax	7.06	24.28	36.50	6.30	3.75	22.10

Reproduced from Petrak, M. L., *Diseases of Cage and Aviary Birds*, by kind permission of Lea & Febiger, Philadelphia, Pennsylvania, 1969.

Vitamin Supplements

ABDEC Drops (manufactured by Parke, Davis, Co.)

0.6 cc (approximately 15 drops) represents:
Vitamin A (palmitate)—5,000 units—1.5 mg
Vitamin B_1 (Thiamin hydrochloride)—1.0 mg
Vitamin B_2 (Riboflavin)—1.2 mg
Vitamin B_6 (Pyridoxine hydrochloride)—1.0 mg
Vitamin C (Ascorbic acid)—50.0 mg
Vitamin D (Ergocalcifero)—400 units—10.0 mg
Nicotinamide (Niacinamide)—10.0 mg
Pantothenic Acid (as the sodium salt)—5.0 mg

Vitamin A & D Oil with Wheat Germ Oil (manufactured by Hartz Mountain Co.)

Ingredients
Cod liver oil, wheat germ oil and a-tocopherol.

Analysis
Vitamin A—400,000 USP units
Vitamin D—40,000 USP units
Vitamin E—900 International units
(This has been fortified with vitamin E to provide the same amount of this vitamin normally found in pure wheat germ oil.)

Nutro Multi-Vitamin, Protein, Mineral Supplement (manufactured by Nutro Products)

Ingredients
Wheat flour, beef meat meal, soybean oil meal, fish meal, wheat germ meal, whole eggs, alfalfa leaf meal, condensed fish solubles, non-fat milk solids, dried buttermilk, fish liver and glandular meal, animal liver meal, dried whey, malt, riboflavin supplement, cod liver oil (1,000 units vitamin A), vitamin D (400 units per gram), wheat germ oil, D activated animal sterol, carotene, charcoal, molasses, vitamin B_{12} feed supplement, niacin, yeast, minerals—Dicalcium phosphate, steamed bone meal, limestone, sodium chloride, iron oxide, manganese sulphate, anise, potassium iodide, copper sulphate, cobalt carbonate, choline chloride, calcium pantothenate, magnesium, silicum, iron sulphate.

Analysis
Protein (min)—20%
Fat (min)—3.75%
Fibre (max)—1.92%
Moisture (max)—9.0%
Carbohydrates—52.0%

Vionate (manufactured by E. R. Squibb & Sons, Inc.)

Ingredients
Degermed corn meal, dibasic calcium phosphate, calcium carbonate, sodium chloride, choline chloride, ascorbic acid (as sodium ascorbate), ferrous carbonate, magnesium oxide, niacin, calcium pantothenate, riboflavin, BHT as a preservative, dl-a-tocopheryl acetate, vitamin A palmitate, thiamin mononitrate, manganous oxide, cupric sulphate, calcium iodate, pyridoxine hydrochloride, cobalt carbonate, folic acid, D activated animal sterol, vitamin B_{12} (as cyanocobalamin).

Vionate should be kept tightly closed, stored at room temperature, and excessive heat (40 °C—104 °F) should be avoided.

British Sources of American Products

All Purina products are available from Ralston Purina, c/o Jenks Brothers Ltd, Castle House, 71/75 Desborough Road, High Wycombe, Buckinghamshire.

Carophyll Red is supplied by Roche Products Ltd, Standard Laboratories, 51 Castle Street, Reading, Berkshire.

Gevral Supplement can be obtained from Barry Kiley, Petcenta, 235 Broadway, Southall, Middlesex.

Australian Equivalent Products and their Sources

Petvite—vitamin-mineral powder. Marrickville Holdings Ltd, IGY Veterinary Products, 74 Edinburgh Road, Marrickville, New South Wales.

Vitemol—vitamin A and D_3 supplement. Nicholas Pty Ltd, 699 Warrigal Road, Chadstone, Victoria.

The following feeds are available from Allied Feeds, 42 Walker Street, Rhodes, New South Wales. (Mailing address: PO Box 65, PO Concord 2137.)

Medicated Starter Crumbles
Medicated Grower Crumbles
Layer Mash
Layer Pellets
Challenger Mash
Challenger Pellets
Challenger Crumbles
'Laymor' Mash
'Laymor' Pellets
'Laymor' Crumbles
Cage Layer All Mash
Cage Layer All Mash Pellets
Cage Layer All Mash Crumbles
Checker Mix Mash
Checker Mix Pellets

Poultry Breeder Mash
Poultry Breeder Crumbles
Chick 'Boosta' Crumbles
Chick Starter Mash
Chick Starter Crumbles
Pullet Developer Mash
Pullet Developer Crumbles
Pullet Grower Mash
Pullet Grower Crumbles
Broiler Starter Crumbles
Broiler Finisher Crumbles
Turkey Breeder Pellets 'E'
Turkey Grower Pellets 'E'
Turkey Finisher Pellets 'E'
Rabbit Pellets

APPENDIX II
Propagation of Suggested Live Foods

Comfrey

Comfrey is a perennial herb, coming up each spring and dying down in the autumn. It likes deep, rich, well-drained soil. It is usually grown from root cuttings. As it is a rank grower, it needs plenty of good mulch or fertilizer. Chicken manure and cow manure are excellent. It takes full sun to partial shade and an average amount of water.

For maximum production, the flower stalks should be kept cut and it should be mulched each spring with rich compost. It is the only known plant to extract vitamin B_{12} from the soil. The plants should not be allowed to make flowers or to go to seed. Irrigation will encourage new growth and leaves.

Analysis of comfrey in dry state (*Henry Doubleday Research Assn*)
Moisture—13.42%
Fat—2.22%
Protein—22.30%
Carbohydrates—37.62%
Crude Fibre—9.38%
Ash—15.06%.

Analysis of minerals
Iron—0.016%
Manganese—0.072%
Calcium—1.7%
Phosphorus—0.82%.

Note: Plants and roots are available from herb specialists.

Earthworm culture (*Lumbricus terrestris*)

Earthworms are burrowing terrestrial worms. They are bisexual, each worm having both male and female characteristics. One can breed with any other worm but not within itself. Two worms may start a culture. To breed they join together at a spot on their bodies where there is a slight swelling (about one-third of their length) and remain together for some time if undisturbed.

When they pull apart one egg capsule is deposited. In twenty-one days, one to twenty small worms will hatch from this egg capsule. The worms are white and can be distinguished easily from maggots or grubs as the worms are about the size of fine jeweller's wire and round. In three months these worms mature and will start to breed. A worm will breed every week. In ninety days a pair of worms may produce 1,000 offspring.

A breeding unit can be any size and shape. A box containing a soil mix of: $\frac{1}{4}$ sand, $\frac{1}{4}$ rabbit manure (or other manure), $\frac{1}{4}$ loamy soil and $\frac{1}{4}$ peat moss, is suggested. This should be well mixed and watered thoroughly. Every three days the mixture should be turned and sprinkled. At the end of nine or ten days, if most of the heat is gone (feel with your hand), it can be used and worms introduced. A small amount of lime or milogranite can be added to keep the mixture from becoming sour.

The temperature in the mixture should be between 19° and 24°C (66° to 75 °F). Deep shade is best although worms can be raised without shade if the climate is not too hot. All household garbage, ground finely, can be added to large units. Carrot trimmings, potato peelings, lettuce and cabbage are all excellent.

To protect the worms in your garden or breeding unit, avoid chemical fertilizers, as they do kill worms. Use natural fertilizers or sludge products.

Fruit flies (*Drosophila melanogaster*)

One of the simplest and best methods of raising fruit flies is to use very ripe fruits as an attraction and as a medium for breeding. If simple rules are followed, *Drosophila* can be raised in abundance. The flies produced will supply not only the necessary protein balance for the birds but also much needed exercise as the flies are captured.

We suggest clean five-gallon containers such as vegetable-oil cans or buckets. The top of the can should be removed and holes should be punched in the bottom to provide drainage for any liquid which forms. Cut and form some hardware cloth to provide a low platform which is placed about two inches from the bottom of the container. Reed fencing, bamboo fencing or similar material should line the inside edge of the can to provide a suitable area upon which the larvae can crawl and pupate.

A lid should be made of small mesh hardware cloth and formed in such a way that it fits into the inside of the can and no edges protrude beyond the can.

When this has been completed, cut over-ripe fruits and squeeze them. Then place a substantial amount of these fruits on the platform inside the can. Avoid fruits which mould quickly and spoil the culture, such as the blue mould of citrus fruit. Bananas are by far the best media for *Drosophila*. A number of these cultures should be prepared and allowed to stand in an area where they will attract fruit flies. After a quantity of insects has entered the cans, the lids should be covered with pieces of mosquito netting and fastened securely so that the flies cannot escape.

The containers should then be placed in a warm place or room at a temperature of 24°C (75 °F). Within ten days they will be swarming with fruit flies. The covered cultures can then be placed in the aviary, preferably behind plantings, where they will be hidden from the public, and the mosquito netting removed. The birds will pounce on the flies as they emerge from the cans.

After the flies have all emerged from the containers, they should be removed from the aviary and the cycle begun again. A continuous supply should be provided, so all containers should not be placed in the aviary at one time. It is also necessary to add new fruits to the containers two or three times weekly, since the fruit will become dry and will not attract the flies.

Usually the draining of the juices from the ripe fruit will pose no problem, but if large quantities of fruit are used a single hole may be provided into which a piece of plastic hose is securely placed in order to carry off the juices. A cork or plug inserted into a hole near the bottom of the container will serve the same purpose.

During the cold months, a wooden box lined with glass wool insulation and large enough to contain the metal container may be provided. Two 40-Watt electric light bulbs should be provided to furnish the necessary heat in the box to keep the fruit flies alive.

In many research laboratories cultures of *Drosophila* are propagated in *Drosophila* culture mediums. Stock cultures are grown in half-pint and quarter-pint bottles in temperature-controlled laboratories in most universities and colleges for genetic studies. Where large numbers of fruit flies are required, these laboratories are an excellent source for additional *Drosophila* breeding stock to seed depleting cultures in small operations.

The principal requirements of a good culture medium are (1) a sufficient amount of sugar to feed the larvae and promote the growth of yeast, and (2) a proper consistency. The first element may be supplied by any one of a variety of fruits, such as bananas, raisins or prunes, by molasses or Karo syrup, or by cane sugar; the necessary body is achieved by cooking with cereals or agar, or both. The foods most widely used are banana medium, cornmeal medium, cornmeal-molasses-rolled oats medium and cream of wheat medium.

Any of the above media should be poured into sterilized containers as soon as they are ready. The most common containers are half-pint or quarter-pint milk bottles. While pouring the food, avoid spilling on the top or sides of the bottles. In each bottle place a strip of paper towelling with one end in the food, to provide an additional surface onto which the larvae can crawl to pupate. Cover the bottles with cheese-cloth and let stand, preferably in a refrigerator, until the food has cooled and the bottles have dried out. If necessary, wipe excessive moisture from the insides of the bottles before plugging them. Plug with unwaxed milk-bottle caps or cotton batting. If only waxed caps are available, perforate them with a needle to admit air.

We have used the cornmeal *Drosophila* medium for thirteen years and are well pleased with it.

Drosophila Medium—Cornmeal Agar
Water—8.50 litres
Agar—92 g
Cornmeal—858 g
Dried Yeast—155 g
Dextrose, anhydrous—516 g
Sucrose—258 g

In large container, with low heat, heat 6.6 litres of water to boiling, add agar and simmer until dissolved. Add yeast and stir until no lumps remain. Mix cornmeal with 1.9 litres of cold water before adding to hot mixture. Stir and let simmer for 25 to 30 minutes. Turn off flame and add sugars and mixture A. Mix well and pour into desired containers.

Mixture A (formulated by Genetics Department, San Diego State University, San Diego, California)
To 836 ml of Proprionic acid (J. T. Baker No. 0286) add 164 ml of water
To 83 ml of Phosphoric acid (J. T. Baker No. 0260) add 917 ml of water
Combine the solutions and store in closed bottle. This solution is an excellent mould retardant.

Potato Formula for Fruit Flies

Mix 1 tablespoon of sugar with a cup of Dried Instant Potatoes. $\frac{1}{2}$ inch of the dry mix is put in the bottom of a litre jar and water poured in to the same level as the top of the mix.

The potato quickly reconstitutes to 'mashed potato'. It is then lightly sprinkled with dry yeast and the jar is left open in the bird room until a fair population of stray flies has gathered on the medium. A square of plastic wrapping film is placed over the mouth of the jar and held down with a rubber band.

The plastic top is freely perforated with pin holes for ventilation. As soon as pupae begin to appear on the glass sides, the container may be placed into an aviary. Half a dozen holes may be made in the cover with a pencil to allow the *Drosophila* to escape as they wish, but the cover prevents small birds from falling into the jars and also keeps the medium or formula moist for about two weeks.

Ten or twelve jars may be used in an aviary and fruit flies are available to the birds at any time. Although the Honeycreepers, Honey-eaters, Tanagers and Zosterops seem to work on them constantly, the supply seems abundant.

Grasshoppers and Locusts

Grasshoppers and locusts are excellent food for many birds. The newly-hatched hoppers are a convenient size for the smallest birds and the adults are a rich source of protein for the larger insectivorous birds. If the correct temperature (30 °C—86 °F) can be maintained, they are easy to breed. Their life cycle is about ten weeks. The eggs take fourteen days to hatch and the non-flying hoppers go through five different moults, the last one after seven days. Mature females may lay eggs four weeks after their last moult.

In the summer months and well into autumn, grasshoppers can usually be collected along roadsides and in grassy areas. They are usually abundant in fields of corn and other row-crops. A good insect or butterfly net can be used to capture them. It is easy with a little practice to swing the net in a wide circle that passes through the top of grassy vegetation. End each swing with a turn of the handle so that the bag hangs over the rim, thus closing the net and preventing the insects from jumping or crawling out. The hoppers should then be emptied into a glass jar with a perforated lid for air and oxygen exchange. The jar should be kept cool and out of the sun and the insects transferred to larger quarters as soon as possible.

To prevent escape and for easier handling, the jar can be put in the refrigerator for twelve to fifteen minutes and the insects will be immobilized or sluggish. Most grasshoppers become recovered from the chilling in two to three minutes so transferring them to their breeding cage must be done quickly.

Locust cages can be purchased from laboratory supply firms, or they may be made easily at home. Plywood boxes with windowscreen wire fronts and a sleeved opening made out of nylon have proved satisfactory. Others that have proven practical are small cages made entirely out of window screening. A metal lid serves as a base. A piece of screen about 30 cm by 40 cm can be rolled into a cylinder 30 cm high which will fit into the lid. The ends of the cylinder should be fastened with staples or two or three pieces of fishing line or fine wire to hold it in shape. A small plate is used on top to keep the insects from escaping. A cage this small can be placed in a refrigerator easily for a few minutes to make the insects dormant if they must be caught or handled.

A larger cage of the same general design may be more practical. Simply make a cylinder 45 cm high by rolling lengthwise a piece of screen wire 45 cm by 75 cm. This cylinder can have a metal cake tin about 22 cm in diameter for a base. The floor of the cage should be covered with paper or a thin layer of dry sand. For the top, use a dish or piece of glass.

Washing the cage twice a week with hot soapy water will prevent disease among the insects. Change the paper on the bottom of the cage every time the cage is washed. If sand is used instead of paper, use fresh sand weekly. When kept in screen cages, grasshoppers seem to benefit from a few hours of sunlight each day. If this is not possible, place a 25-Watt incandescent bulb 15 to 20 cm from the cage to provide warmth.

If the grasshoppers gather on the side nearest the bulb, it may be too far away. If they appear to avoid the heat, it may be too close. In aquaria with glass sides, grasshoppers may be overheated and die from artificial lighting.

Food is easily provided. The three favourite foods are lettuce leaves, sliced apples and various kinds of grasses. Clover, wheat grass (*Agropyrum*), and bluegrass (*Poa*) are all acceptable to grasshoppers or locusts. Celery with tops intact is also useful. The insects will also eat bran flakes.

A good practice is to grow the food plants in thumb pots; then the entire pot can be put into the cage. Another practice is to put fresh-cut leaves of spinach, chard, comfrey and other acceptable plants in the cage. As soon as they are cut the leaves are put in water in a small-mouthed container so the insects cannot fall into the water. The container is then put into the cage.

A small water vial plugged with a large diameter dental roll (from any dentist's office) should be prepared daily as a source of water. This vial should be tilted at an angle and placed on the floor of the cage. It can be supported with a little modelling clay. The water should be changed daily.

When grasshoppers and locusts are set up for breeding, they need special care. In the breeding cage, a container of sterilized sand should be provided. This sand should be sterilized in an oven at a temperature of 177 °C (350 °F) for three hours. The sand should be spread out in a pan at a depth of no more than 2.54 cm. A glass jar with the top covered with aluminium foil should be placed in the oven at the same time. After the three-hour heating period, the sand should be cooled in the oven and placed in the sterilized jar immediately and kept covered with the foil until needed.

Grasshoppers and locusts lay from 20 to 150 eggs in soil or sand. A deep finger bowl or soup bowl should be filled with some of the sterilized sand. The sand should be wet thoroughly and any excess water drained off. The bowl of sand is then placed in the cage. The sand should be kept moist with a few drops of water sprinkled on it once or twice a day.

After a few days or a week, remove the bowl of sand from the cage and strain the sand through an ordinary kitchen sieve to find egg pods. If any are present, re-bury them in the sand, and the bowl should then be placed in a separate cage in a shaded part of a warm room. Continue to keep the sand moist at all times. Some young will hatch during this time.

The young grasshoppers can be fed in the same manner as the adults, however they do need a little more humidity. A second container of wet sand placed in their cage will supply the needed water vapour. The young eat continuously and grow rapidly when abundant food is provided.

Hydroponic Grasses

Hydroponic grass is a very complete nutritional food supplement, since it is high in proteins, vitamins and trace minerals. An important consideration is that the grass produced in hydroponic units is relatively free of any insecticide or pesticide residue, which in all probability occurs in high concentration in many commercial vegetables. Hydroponic grass is also free of foreign bodies, such as wires, nails or glass which is occasionally picked up in the harvesting of field plants.

The hydroponic unit we have used contains four racks, each with 56 plastic trays ($29 \times 61 \times 5$ cm) for a total of 224 trays. Approximately two and one half pounds of certified oat or barley seed is placed in each of 32 trays daily, and the trays returned to the racks. Water containing plant nutrients is sprayed over the seed at six to eight hour intervals. The temperature of the unit is maintained at 17–19°C (64–68°F) by an air conditioner, and light from fluorescent tubes is continuous. After seven days of germination and growth, the grass which has attained a height of five to seven inches is harvested and the trays are then replanted. This maintains a continuous supply for the many young birds which thrive on this food.

Analysis of 6.8 kg of 7-day hydroponic grass (Wisconsin Research Foundation)
Vitamin A—91.143 I.U. (International Units)
Vitamin E—68.4 mg
Riboflavin—31.2 mg
Niacin—145.0 I.U.
Vitamin B₁ Thiamin—18 mg
Vitamin C—6111 I.U.
Calcium—0.022%
Phosphorus—0.047%
Water—90.77%
Dry Matter—9.33%
Ether Extract (fat)—0.48%
Nitrogen-free extract—3.95%
Fibre—2.41%
Ash—0.26%
Trace minerals—abundant
Enzymes—abundant.

Mealworms

Mealworms are an extremely valuable source of live food for insectivorous birds, and are invaluable during the breeding season. Breeding stock of mealworms may be ordered from reliable dealers who advertise in many game-breeding and avicultural journals. Although mealworms may be purchased in commercial quantities, their care is extremely simple and breeding colonies are easy to maintain.

Mealworm containers may be any metal, plastic, glass, etc. container which has smooth sides so that the worms cannot crawl out. A solid top or lid should not be used on the container as the insects must have air. A fine windowscreen wire is excellent for the covering. If wooden boxes are used, they must be lined with light-weight metal on the bottom and sides to prevent escape.

A layer of dry red wheat bran or barley meal 10 to 15 cm in depth should be placed in the bottom of the container. A piece of standard burlap (jute or hemp woven fabric) feed sack is laid on top of the bran to provide security and restrictive lighting which the insects need when breeding.

Between the layers of the burlap or fabric slices of sweet potato, carrots, apples or banana skins are added to provide needed moisture in the container. In dry climates it may be necessary to moisten the fabric with water in a clothes sprayer.

After the breeding stock is placed in the container it should not be disturbed. The mealworms do best when not disturbed too frequently. The adult beetle lays about fifty bean-shaped white eggs, covered with a sticky secretion which causes the bran or meal to adhere to them. In about two weeks the eggs hatch into slender white larvae or worms, which soon turn yellow. The fully-grown worms are yellow, shading to a yellowish-brown at the articulation of each segment. The mealworms crawl into the layers of sacking and change into the pupae stage, the third stage. The pupae then change into the adult beetle and the cycle is repeated.

Adult beetles measure about 11 mm in length and normally live about three months. The larvae reach maturity in about ninety days and then turn into the pupae stage. In another two weeks the pupae will emerge as young beetles. Cultures grow best in room temperatures of 27 °C (80 °F).

Laboratory Mice—Breeding Colonies

The albino mice used in laboratories and for food by aviculturists have been bred from albino mutants of ordinary house mice (*Mus musculus*). Mice can be purchased from pet shops, commercial breeders, etc. However, mice are extremely expensive for aviculturists or zoological gardens, where as many as 3,000 may be fed yearly.

Mouse colonies can be established and mice can live in various kinds of cages. The height of a mouse cage need be only 15 cm. A small cage is suitable for breeding and nursing. A pair of mice with a dozen young can be kept for a few days in a cage 30 by 15 cm. As the young grow, a larger cage should be provided. A good rule is that each mouse requires a minimum of 75 sq cm.

Mice are easily kept in home-made cages made from a metal box or bin. A water bottle should be placed on the top of the cage with a drinking tube extending 5 or 6 cm through the top of the cage so the mice can reach it easily. The floor of the cage should be completely covered with sterilized wood shavings, shredded paper or commercial litter. Mites and lice can be eradicated by dusting adult mice with pyrethrin. Young mice should not be exposed to dusting powder which contains rotenone or lindane powder. Dusting powder may also be applied to bedding material except in cages where babies are nursing.

Fresh drinking water should be provided daily. Most mice drink 6 or 7 ml of water daily, if fed dry food. Water bottles are offered for sale in most pet shops. Glass tubing for these bottles with an inside diameter of 6–9 mm is made especially for mice. The end of the glass tubing from which the mouse drinks should measure 3 mm. If too large, the water bottle may leak. Water bottles and tubes are washed with hot soapy water and after thorough rinsing are dried in direct sunlight. The cages should be washed in the same way, monthly or weekly as the need arises.

Like water, food should be available at all times. Excellent commercial food is manufactured and small quantities may be purchased from pet stores. Food baskets made of ½-inch mesh are usually suspended from the top of the cage, or hung along the side of the cage near the top. The mice pull the pellets through the mesh, preventing contamination of food which occurs when pellets are placed in open bowls or dishes. One mouse will eat about 5 grams of dry food a day.

Mice colonies should be housed in rooms with a temperature close to 24°C (75°F), free of draught, with a relative humidity of 50 per cent. A smooth cement floor will provide easy cleaning and minimum rodent odours.

The lifecycle of mice is short. Nineteen days after mating, the young are born. The average litter is five to six young. A female may have up to eight litters a year. Mice are used as breeders in a colony for ten or twelve months and then are replaced by young stock. Mice are mature at two months of age and will begin reproduction at that time.

A small cardboard box or cigar box turned upside-down and with one end open may be placed in the breeding cage for a nest. Shredded paper, dried grass or towelling will be carried into the nest to keep the babies warm. The babies are born naked (hence the term 'pinky') and are quite helpless. The eyes open at twelve to fourteen days. The mother nurses the young for about thirty days and at this age they begin feeding themselves. Several litters of mice of the same age may be housed together when they can forage for themselves.

Purina Mouse Chow (Manufactured by Ralston Purina Co.)

Ground rolled yellow corn, ground wheat, dried skimmed milk, fish meal, brewers' dried yeast, soybean meal, corn oil, animal fat preserved with BHA, vitamin A supplement, vitamin B_{12} supplement, D activated plant sterol, menthionine hydroxy analogue, vitamin E supplement, calcium pantothenate, choline chloride, niacin, iodized salt, calcium carbonate, zinc oxide, manganous oxide, copper sulphate, ferrous sulphate.

Trees, Shrubs and Plants visited by Hummingbirds

Abutilon (Flowering Maple)
Acacia
Agave
Aloe
Aquilegia (Columbine)
Begonia
Beloperone (Shrimp plant)
Bromelia
Cactus family
Calliandra
Callistemon (Bottle-brush)
Cereus
Chilopsis (Desert willow)
Chrysanthemum
Cetru blossoms
Clematis
Crotolaria (Canary bird bush)
Dahlia
Delphinium
Dombeya (Pink ball)
Eucalyptus

Fuschia
Gladiolas
Godetia
Grevillea (Hummingbird bush)
Hakea (sea urchin)
Hemerocallis (daylilies)
Hibiscus
Most fruit trees
Impatiens
Iris
Jasmine
Lantana
Lobelia
Lonicera
Lotus
Lupine
Malvastrum (False mallow)
Melianthus (Honey bush)
Nicotiana
Orchid family
Parkinsonia

Passiflora
Penstemon
Petunia
Phlox
Pittosporum
Poinciana
Portulaca
Rhododendron

Robinia
Salvia
Scrophularia
Strelitzia (Bird of Paradise)
Syringa (Lilac)
Verbena
Yucca

APPENDIX III
Metric Conversion Table

1 millimetre = 0.0394 inch
1 centimetre = 0.394 inch
1 metre = 3.28 feet
1 inch = 2.54 cm
1 foot = 30.48 cm

1 hectare = 2.471 acres
1 acre = 0.405 hectares

1 litre = 1.76 pints
10 litres = 2.2 gallons
1 pint = 0.568 litres
1 gallon = 4.546 litres

1 gram = 0.0353 oz
1 kilogram = 2.2 lb
1 oz = 28.35 g
1 lb = 0.454 kg

Diet for Cockatoo Chicks

Measurements by volume, not weight. Use standard measuring cup and spoon.

½ cup wheat hearts cereal
⅛ teaspoon salt
½ teaspoon fine cuttlefish bone meal
1 teaspoon Karo corn syrup
2 fresh egg yolks
milk or water
4 drops ABDEC vitamin supplement

Mix dry ingredients, add syrup and egg yolks, then milk or water to make a souplike mixture; boil over low heat for 3 to 5 minutes, stirring gently. Cool until finger warm; add 4 drops ABDEC and stir in feed mixture with spoon.

Wheat Hearts manufactured by General Mills Inc. Sperry Operations, Palo Alto, CA.94303. Ingredients: Wheat flour, ground wheat, and wheat germ meal.

Crude protein, not less than 14.2%
Crude fat, not less than 3.3%
Crude fibre, not more than 5.4%
N F E, not less than 70.7%
Ash, not more than 1.4%

ABDEC Drops manufactured by Parke, Davis & Co., Detroit, Michigan. 0.6cc (approximately 15 drops) represent:

Vitamin A (Palitate) – 5,000 units	1.5mg
Vitamin B1 (Thiamine Hydrochloride)	1.0mg
Vitamin B2 (Riboflavin)	1.2mg
Vitamin B6 (Pyridoxine Hydrochloride)	1.0mg
Vitamin C (Ascorbic Acid)	50.0mg
Vitamin D (Erocalcifero) – 400 units	10.0mg
Nicotiramide (Niacinamide)	10.0mg
Pantothenic acid (as the sodium salt)	5.0mg

One hundred and seventy five species of psittacines have been raised successfully on this dish.

BIBLIOGRAPHY

Allen, G. M., *Birds and Their Attributes*, Dover Publications, New York, 1962

Austin Jr, O. and Singer, A., *Families of Birds*, Golden Press, Inc., New York, 1971

Austin Jr, O. and Singer, A., *Birds of the World*, Golden Press, Inc., New York, 1961

Bannerman, D. A., *Birds of West and Equatorial Africa*, Vols 1 and 2, Oliver & Boyd, Edinburgh, 1953

Barret, Charles, *Parrots of Australia*, N. H. Seward, Pty, Melbourne, 1949

Bates, H., Busenbark, R., *Finches and Soft-billed Birds*, T. F. H. Publications, Jersey City, New Jersey, 1970

Bates, H., Busenbark, R., *Parrots*, T. F. H. Publications, Jersey City, New Jersey, 1959

Bellrose, F. C., *Ducks, Geese & Swans of North America*, Stackpole Books, Harrisburg, Pennsylvania, 1976

Bent, A. C., *Life Histories of North American Gulls and Terns*, Dodd Mead & Co., New York, 1947

Blake, E. R., *Birds of Mexico*, Chicago Univ. Press, Chicago, Illinois, 1953

Bond, J., *Birds of the West Indies*, Houghton Mifflin Co., New York, 1961

Boosey, E. J., *Foreign Bird Keeping*, Poultry World, Ltd, London, 1958

Brandt, H., *Arizona and Its Bird Life*, Bird Research Foundation, Ohio, 1951

Bridges, William, *The Bronx Zoo Book of Wild Animals*, E. P. Dutton and Co., New York, 1968

Brown, L., Amadon, D., *Eagles, Hawks and Falcons of the World*, Vols 1 and 2, Feltham, English Country Life Books, 1968

Brown, R. W., *Composition of Scientific Words*, Reese Press, New Jersey, 1956

Burton, J. A., *Owls of the World*, E. P. Dutton & Co., New York, 1973

Butler, A. G., *Foreign Birds for Cage and Aviary*, Vols 1 and 2, Feathered World, London, 1901

Cayley, N. W., *What Bird is That?* Angus & Robinson, London, 1951

Collins Jr, H. H., *Complete Field Guide to American Wildlife*, Harper and Brothers, New York, 1959

Curran, C. H., *Insects of the Pacific World*, Washington Infantry Journal Press, Washington DC, 1945

Davis, L. I., *A Field Guide to the Birds of Mexico and Central America*, University of Texas Press, Austin, 1972

Delacour, J. T., *Currassows and Related Birds*, American Museum of Natural History, New York, 1973

Delacour, J. T., *Pheasant Breeding & Care*, T. F. H. Publications, Inc., New Jersey, 1953

Delacour, J. T., *Pheasants of the World*, Charles Scribner's Sons, New York, 1951

Delacour, J. T., *Waterfowl of the World*, Vols 1 and 2, Country Life Ltd, London, 1954, 1956

DeSchaunensee, R. M., *The Birds of Colombia*, Livingston Publishing Co., Narbeth, Pennsylvania, 1964

DeSchaunensee, R. M., *A Guide to the Birds of South America*, Livingston Publishing Co., Wynnewood, Pennsylvania, 1970

Eastman, Jr, W. R., *The Parrots of Australia*, Angus & Robinson Ltd, Sydney, Australia, 1966

Falla, R. A., *A Field Guide to the Birds of New Zealand*, Collins Publishing Co., London, 1966

Fisher, J. and Peterson, R. T., *The World of Birds*, Garden City, New York, 1964

Forshaw, J. M., *Parrots of the World*, Doubleday & Co., New York, 1973

Gilliard, E. T., *Birds of Paradise and Bower Birds*, Natural History Press, New York, 1969

Gilliard, E. T., *Living Birds of the World*, Doubleday & Co., Inc., New York, 1958

Gill, L. A., *First Guide to South African Birds*, Maskew Miller Ltd, Cape Town, South Africa, 1956

Goodwin, D., *Pigeons and Doves of the World*, Staples Printers Ltd, London, 1970

Graf, A. B., *Exotica*, Roehres Publishing Co., New Jersey, 1963

Greenwalt, C. H., *Hummingbirds*, Doubleday & Co., Inc., New York, 1960

Grzimek, H. C. B., *Animal Life Encyclopedia*, Vols. 6, 7 and 8, Van Nostrand and Reinhold, New York, 1972, 1973

Hamlet, John, *Birds of Prey of the World*, Clarkson N. Potter, Inc., New York, 1964

Harris, Michael, *A Field Guide to the Birds of the Galapagos*, William Collins & Sons Ltd, London, 1974

Hayward, Jim, *Lovebirds and their Colour Mutations*, Blandford Press, Poole, 1979

Herklotts, G. A. C., *The Birds of Trinidad and Tobago*, Collins & Sons Ltd, London, 1961

Hill, Robin, *Australian Birds*, Thomas Nelson & Sons, Melbourne, 1970

Hill, Leonard, *Penguin Millionaire*, David & Charles Ltd, London, 1976

Hyde, D. O., *Raising Wild Ducks in Captivity*, E. P. Dutton & Co., New York, 1974

Immelmann, Claus, *Australian Finches*, Angus & Robinson, London, 1965

Jaeger, E. C., *A Source Book of Biological Names and Terms*, Charles C. Thomas, Illinois, 1944

Johnsgard, P. A., *Waterfowl of North America*, Indiana University Press, Indiana, 1975

Johnsgard, P. A., *Waterfowl*, University of Nebraska Press, Lincoln, 1968

Lendon, Alan, *Australian Parrots in Field and Aviary*, Angus & Robinson, Sydney, 1973

Lekagul, Boonsong, *Bird Guide of Thailand*, Association for the Conservation of Wildlife, 1968

Low, Rosemary, *The Parrots of South America*, John Gifford Ltd, London, 1972

Low, Rosemary, *Lories and Lorikeets*, Paul Elek Ltd, London, 1977

Low, Rosemary, *Parrots—Their Care and Breeding*, Blandford Press, Poole, 1980

McGregor, R. C., *A Manual of Philippine Birds*, Dept of the Interior, Bureau of Science, Manila, 1909

Naether, Carl, *Soft-billed Bird*, All-Pet Books, Inc., Wisconsin, 1955

Officer, H. R., *Australian Honeyeaters*, Arbuckle, Waddell Ltd, Melbourne, 1975

Pearson, T. G., *Birds of America*, Garden City Publishing Co., New York, 1936

Peters, J. L., *Checklist of Birds of the World*, Harvard Univ. Press, Cambridge, Massachusetts, Vol. 1, 1931, Vol. 13, 1970

Popenoe, W., *Manual of Tropical and Subtropical Fruits*, Macmillan Co., New York, 1924

Petrak, M. L., *Diseases of Cage and Aviary Birds*, Lea & Febiger, Philadelphia, Pennsylvania, 1969

Rand, A. and Gilliard, E. T., *Handbook of New Guinea Birds*, Weidenfeld and Nicolson, London, 1967.

Roberts, Austin, *The Birds of South Africa*, H. F. & G. Witherby, Ltd, London, 1953

Robbins, C. S., Brunn, B. and Zim, H. S., *Birds of North America*, Golden Press, New York, 1966

Rutgers, A., Norris, K., *Encyclopedia of Aviculture*, Vols 1, 2 and 3, Blandford Press, London, 1970, 1972, 1977

Scheithauer, Walter, *Hummingbirds*, Thomas Y. Crowell Co., New York, 1967

Slater, Peter, *A Field Guide to Australian Birds*, Vols 1 and 2, Rigby Ltd, Adelaide, 1970, 1974

Skead, C. J., *Sunbirds of South Africa*, Cape & Transvaal Printers Ltd, Cape Town, 1967

Silvan, James, *Raising Laboratory Animals*, Natural History Press, New York, 1936

Smith, L. H., *The Lyrebird*, Lansdown Press Ltd, Melbourne, 1968

Smithes, B. E., *The Birds of Borneo*, Oliver and Boyd Ltd, London, 1960

Sparks, J. and Soper, T., *Penguins*, David and Charles Ltd, Great Britain, 1967

Szanton, J. G., *Food Values and Calorie Charts*, Laylen Offset Press, New York, 1958

Taylor, N., *Practical Encyclopedia of Gardening*, Garden City Publishing Co., New York, 1938

Thornton, Ian, *Darwin's Islands*, Natural History Press, New York, 1971

Todd, F. S., *Waterfowl, Ducks, Geese & Swans of the World*, Sea World Press, San Diego, 1979

Vane, E. N. T., *Guide to Lovebirds and Parrotlets*, Iliffe Books Inc., London, 1967

Van Tyne, J. and Berger, A. J., *Fundamentals of Ornithology*, John Wiley and Sons Inc., New York, 1959

Wakinshaw, Lawrence, *Cranes of the World*, Winchester Press, New York, 1973

Wayre, Philip, *A Guide to Pheasants of the World*, Country Life Publishing Co., London, 1969

Wetty, J. C., *The Life of Birds*, W. B. Saunders Co., Penna, 1962

Whistler, Hugh, *Popular Handbook of Indian Birds*, Gurney & Jackson Publishing Co., London, 1949

Wildash, P., *Birds of Vietnam*, C. E. Tuttle & Co., Rutland, Vermont, 1968

Williams, J. G., *The Birds of East & Central Africa*, Collins Press, London, 1963

Yamashina, Yoshimaro, *Birds of Japan*, Tokyo News Service, Ltd, Japan, 1974

INDEX OF SCIENTIFIC NAMES

INDEX OF COMMON NAMES

[215]

Index of Common Names